Techniques of Differentiation and Integration:

A Program for Self-instruction

Techniques of Differentiation and Integration:

A Program for Self-instruction

Herman Meyer
University of Miami

Robert V. Mendenhall
Ohio Wesleyan University

McGraw-Hill Book Company
New York   St. Louis   San Francisco   Toronto   London   Sydney

Techniques of Differentiation and Integration:
A Program for Self-instruction

Preface

Because programmed materials have not been widely used in teaching college mathematics, we would like to discuss just what this programmed unit is and what it is not.

First, it is not a substitute for a textbook in the Calculus; it makes no claim to cover the full range of subject matter normally taught in a first course in the Calculus. In particular, it does not deal at all with the development of the theory or its motivations or applications. It does not provide the full range of educational experiences which form the objectives of any course in mathematics; it makes no attempt to develop the student's imagination or originality. Nor does it purport to teach the material it does include with greater efficiency than that attained by a competent teacher and textbook.

Instead, this program is intended as a supplement to a teacher and textbook. Its sole purpose is to remove the preoccupation with the techniques of differentiation and integration from the *classroom* and thus significantly increase the classroom time available for the teaching of the theory and applications of the Calculus. It deals only with that part of a calculus course which is the almost automatic application of rules and concepts, and it provides an avenue for the drill necessary to attain proficiency in these more or less routine techniques.

Since this program is not a calculus textbook, definitions sometimes appear in the body of the material without being specifically identified. The function concept is presumed but not in its general form; domains for functions are not exhibited nor are theorems stated precisely. No hint appears of the existence of functions having no derivatives or antiderivatives, nor of the dependence of some integration techniques on the domain of the function. These iniquities were accepted in order to place sole emphasis here on techniques. We trust that the instructor will exploit the class time gained by this program to present precise formulations of the concepts of the Calculus with increased attention to its intuitive foundations and rich applications.

No standard programming style has been followed. The program is linear (nonbranching) and accounts for individual differences only in that the more talented students can proceed at a faster pace. New techniques are first introduced in considerable detail, with the student guided to solutions. Then he is released for further practice and drill. The format, which places answers on the back of the question page, was selected in order to facilitate the mechanics of proceeding through the program. But it introduces an unfortunate temptation for the student which he must continually resist; even a quick glance at an answer before he adequately attacks a problem can vitiate both the value of the problem and the development of his own resources.

The existence of programmed material does not release the teacher from pacing the course of study by assignments and examinations. For this reason a detailed table of contents is included. Since the material is relatively self-contained and independent of an accompanying text, it can be initiated at the very beginning of the course and can thus act to motivate the more precise and systematic development of the Calculus.

Nor does the existence of programmed material release the student from responsibility for his own learning. Each problem deserves pencil, paper, and effort to attain a solution *before* the answer is sought. And each error deserves thoughtful analysis and correction. Otherwise, it is quite possible to "proceed" through the program and learn very little indeed.

A short table of integrals is included, and frequent references to this table appear throughout. These are indicated by the integral symbol $\int$ followed by a number. Thus $\int 17$ indicates a reference to the integral formula numbered 17. It is assumed, particularly for Chap. 1, that the student has access to mathematical tables giving values of the sine and cosine functions (angles measured in radians), of the exponential and logarithmic (naperian) functions, and of the square, cube, and reciprocal functions.

Herman Meyer
Robert V. Mendenhall

Contents

Chapter 4. *Technique of Integration* 57

To The Student

This book has been designed and written to assist you to learn the techniques of integration and differentiation. To be as efficient and useful as possible, it employs a self-instructional technique called programming. Since you may be unfamiliar with this type of presentation, the following notes on programming, its use in this book, and the study suggestions may be of value.

Programmed Books

Essentially, a programmed book is the same as a conventional text in its overall purpose: it attempts to teach certain concepts and to drill in various procedures. But a programmed book is more explicit than most texts in the presentation of ideas, concepts, and manipulations to be learned. By breaking each new idea or skill into a series of logical and carefully graded steps (called "frames") and requiring that you actively respond to each frame, programming increases your participation in learning beyond that normally possible from reading an ordinary text. Actively responding to each frame means that you are not allowed to passively absorb what you read; each frame requires you to do something. The frames are a carefully constructed sequence of items which lead from the simple to the complex and which progressively require that you take more and more responsibility for the operations you are asked to do. You must work a problem and then write the answer to it, decide between alternatives, or otherwise engage in thinking out what the book teaches. The quick knowledge of whether you were right or not in answering a frame keeps you apprised of exactly how much you have learned.

How To Use This Book

Since the organization of this programmed book is unusual, leaf through the pages quickly and note the following features:

The use of right- and left-hand pages

Notice that in the main part of the book, the right-hand page contains the *frames* of the program. Numbered by chapters, they follow a normal sequence through each chapter. Notice also that the back of each right-hand page contains answers (and discussion) to *just* those frames appearing on its front. The answers are keyed to their frames by identical numbers.

Use of color

As a help in comparing answers, the answer page has been printed in color so that the visual contrast between frames and answers will keep their functions separate in your mind.

Information panels

These panels introduce discussions of related materials and ideas into the flow of frames and, like the frames, always appear on the right-hand page. As you will note, the panels are preceded and followed by colored rules, thus separating them from the other parts of the page.

Study Suggestions

The following suggestions should be helpful to you in learning how best to use this book:

1. Read and work the problem presented in each frame (right-hand page only).
2. After having arrived at your *own* answer, write it out in complete form and turn the page to consult the answer and discussion (left-hand page only). If your answer does not agree with the one given, try to find out why, correct your mistake, and then go ahead.
3. An obvious final point: do not consult the answers *before* working the problem and do not look ahead at future answers. Learning is an activity; you must *do* something *yourself*. If you are tempted to browse through the answers given on the left-hand page, use the marker provided in the book to cover the answers below the one you are consulting.

The following graph figures are for your use while working certain sections of the program. They have been grouped in the front of the book for your convenience in referring to them.

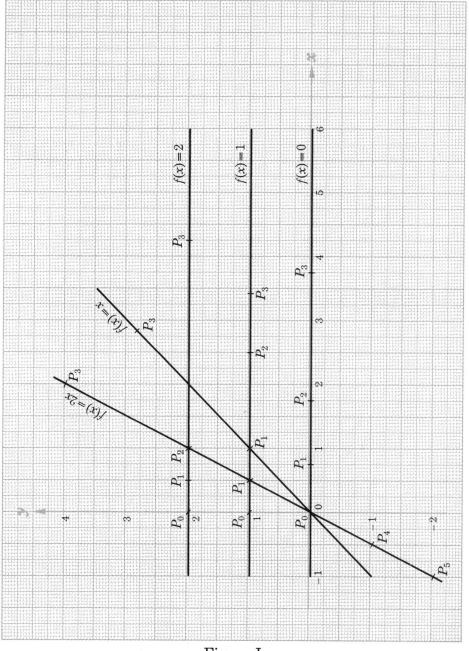

Figure I

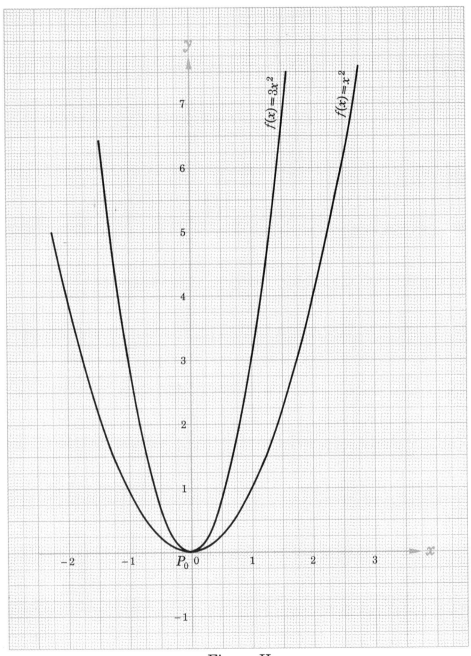

Figure II

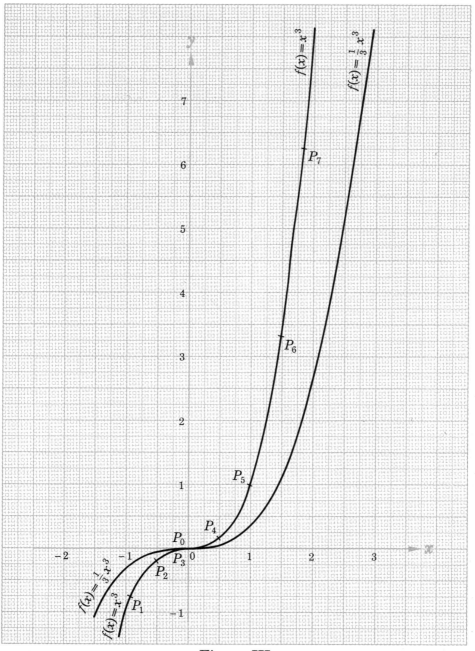

Figure III

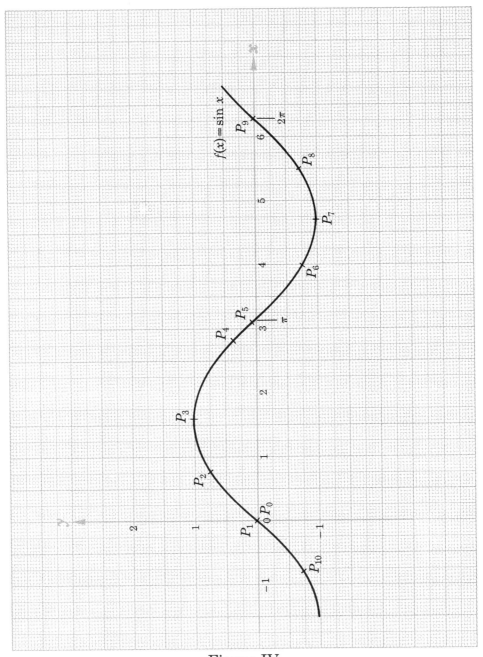

Figure IV

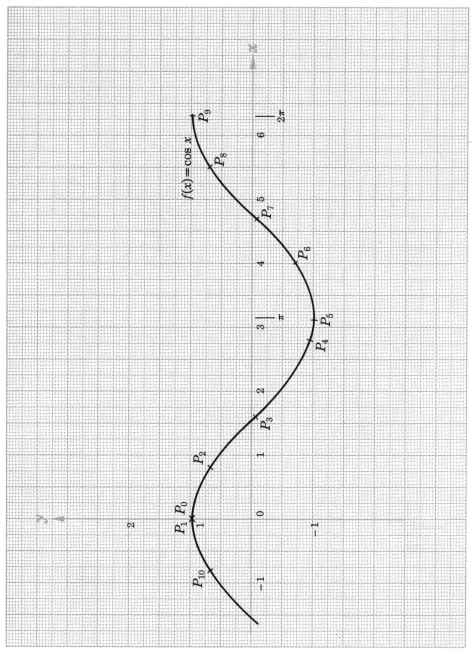

Figure V

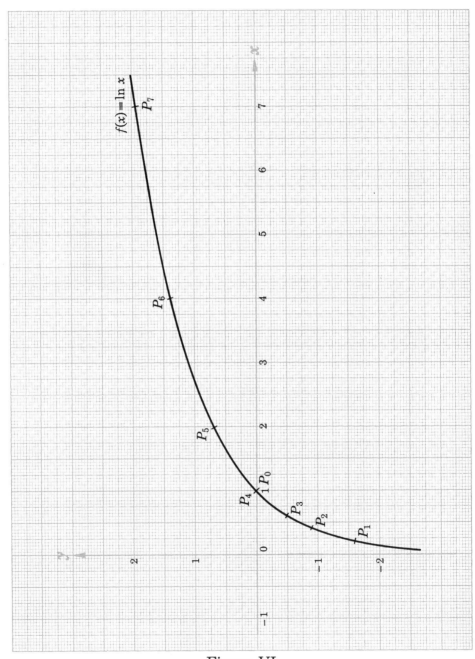

Figure VI

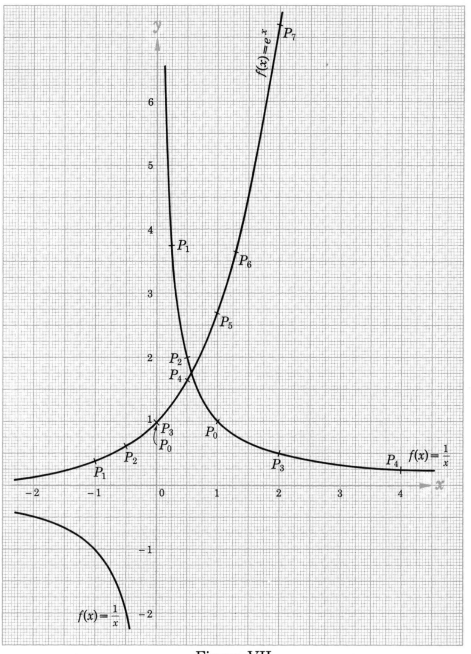

Figure VII

chapter 1

The Slope Curve of a Function; The Derivative

To find the *angle of inclination* of a given line in a coordinate plane:

1 Select any point on the given line,
2 Through this point draw a horizontal line (parallel to the x axis).

The angle of inclination is the smallest *counterclockwise* angle through which the horizontal line need be rotated until it coincides with the given line.

---

1 What is the angle of inclination of a vertical line (parallel to the y axis)?

2 What is the angle of inclination of a horizontal line (parallel to the x axis)?

3 If a line *rises* from left to right, in what quadrant is its angle of inclination?

4 If a line falls from left to right, in what quadrant is its angle of inclination? Is the tangent of its angle of inclination positive or negative?

The *slope of a line* in a coordinate plane is the tangent of its angle of inclination. Thus the *slope* of a nonvertical line is a real *number*.

---

5 What is the slope of the line L?

1 90° or $\pi/2$ radians. Radian measure of angles is most useful for the calculus. Since π radians equals 180°, 1 radian is approximately 57.3°.

2 0 or π radians (0° or 180°), depending on how one interprets the language of the definition of the angle of inclination: smallest counter-clockwise angle. We will select 0 as the angle of inclination of a horizontal line, not π. Thus the angle of inclination θ of any line satisfies the inequality $0 \leqslant \theta < \pi$.

3 First quadrant. Thus, in particular, the tangent of this angle is a positive number.

4 Second quadrant. The tangent of a second-quadrant angle is a negative number. Our primary concern will not be with the angle of inclination of a line but with the *tangent* of this angle.

5 The slope of line L is 2. Its angle of inclination is indicated as θ and $\tan \theta = \frac{2}{1} = 2$.

6 What is the slope of the line M?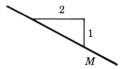

7 What is the slope of a horizontal line (one parallel to the x axis)?

8 Has the concept of *slope* been defined for *all* lines in a coordinate plane?

9 Draw a line having positive slope, i.e., a line whose slope is a positive number.

10 Draw a line having negative slope, i.e., a line whose slope is a negative number.

11 Does a horizontal line have slope?

12 Does a vertical line have an angle of inclination? Slope?

13 Select a point P in a coordinate plane and construct a line passing through it and having slope 1.5.

6 The slope of line M is $-\frac{1}{2}$. Its angle of inclination is represented by θ. Since $\theta = \pi - \alpha$, $\tan \theta = \tan (\pi - \alpha) = -\tan \alpha = -\frac{1}{2}$.

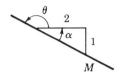

7 0. The angle of inclination of a horizontal line is 0 radians, and $\tan 0 = 0$.

8 No, vertical lines (lines parallel to the y axis) are not included. The angle of inclination of a vertical line is $\pi/2$, which has no tangent.

9 The line must *rise* from left to right, such as:

Its angle of inclination must be a first-quadrant angle.

10 The line must *fall* from left to right, such as:

Its angle of inclination must be a second-quadrant angle.

11 Yes! Its slope is the number 0. Its angle of inclination is 0 radians, and $\tan 0 = 0$.

12 Its angle of inclination is $\pi/2$. Since this angle has no tangent, a vertical line has no slope.

13 From P, go 1 unit to the right, then 1.5 units upward to obtain the point Q. The desired line is drawn through P and Q. The same line is obtained if you first go, say, 10 units to the right, then 15 units upward.

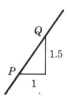

14 Select a point P in a coordinate plane and construct a line passing through it and having slope $-\frac{1}{2}$.

15 Pick a point P in the coordinate plane and construct lines through it having respective slopes 0, $\frac{1}{2}$, 1, 2, $-\frac{1}{3}$, -1, -3. Label each line with its slope and study the resulting diagram. Can you, at a glance, distinguish lines having positive slopes from lines having negative slopes? Lines having slopes numerically greater than 1 from lines having slopes numerically less than 1?

16 By making suitable measurements, compute the slope of each line.

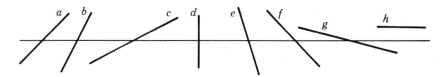

17 Refer to Fig. IV (front of this book). Draw the tangent lines to the curve at each of the points P_1, P_2, P_3, P_4 indicated, and after making suitable measurements, compute the slope of each line.

The graph of a function f is defined to be the set of all points in the coordinate plane having coordinates $[x,f(x)]$. Thus if the function f is defined by the formula (rule) $f(x) = x^2$, then the points $(0,0^2) = (0,0)$; $[\frac{1}{2},(\frac{1}{2})^2] = (\frac{1}{2},\frac{1}{4})$; $(1,1^2) = (1,1)$; $(2,2^2) = (2,4)$; $[-1,(-1)^2] = (-1,1)$; $[-2,(-2)^2] = (-2,4)$ lie on the graph of this function.

18 On a coordinate plane, to the same scale as Fig. II, (a) locate the points listed in the remark above, (b) compute and locate a few more points lying on the graph of the function defined by the formula $f(x) = x^2$, (c) draw a smooth curve connecting the points you have located, and (d) compare with Fig. II.

19 Check a few points on the sine curve of Fig. IV to ensure that it is in fact the graph of the sine function. Use a trigonometric table, but note that angles must be measured in radians.

14 From P, go 1 unit to the right, then $\frac{1}{2}$ unit *downward*. Or, 2 units to the right, then 1 unit *downward*. A line having negative slope *falls* from left to right.

15

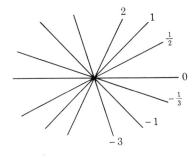

16 Since your measurements are of necessity approximate, your answers can only approximate the following: (*a*) 1; (*b*) 2; (*c*) $\frac{1}{2}$; (*d*) this is a vertical line, it has no slope; (*e*) -3; (*f*) -1; (*g*) $-\frac{1}{4}$; (*h*) 0.

17 Slope of the tangent line at P_1 equals 1; at P_2 it equals 0.7; at P_3 it equals 0; at P_4 it equals -0.94. Again, both the drawing of the tangent lines and the resulting measurements are approximate. It is only expected that your answers will be *approximately* those listed.

18 This is precisely the graph of the function f defined by $f(x) = x^2$.

19 It is the graph of the sine function. For negative values of x, we need the trigonometric relationship $\sin(-x) = -(\sin x)$. For values of x above the range of the table we need apply $\sin(\pi - x) = \sin x$. [Thus, $\sin 2.00 = \sin(3.14 - 2.00) = \sin 1.14$.]

20 From tabulated values of the cosine function verify that Fig. V is the graph of the cosine function.

21 From tabulated values verify that Fig. VI is the graph of the natural-logarithmic function.

22 From tabulated values verify that one of the curves of Fig. VII is the graph of the exponential function e^x.

23 From tabulated values verify that the curve of Fig. II, labeled x^2, is in fact the graph of this function. At the same time check the graph of the function $3x^2$. In order to use such tables to find, say, $(1.7)^2$, write $(1.7)^2 = (\frac{17}{10})^2 = \frac{289}{100} = 2.89$.

24 From tabulated values, check the graph of the functions x^3 and $\frac{1}{3}x^3$ of Fig. III. For negative values, note that $(-x)^3 = -(x^3)$. To find from the tabulated values, say $(1.7)^3$, write $(1.7)^3 = (\frac{17}{10})^3 = \frac{4913}{1000} = 4.913$.

25 From tabulated values check the graph of the reciprocal function $1/x$ in Fig. VII.

26 Check the graphs of Fig. I.

27 Throughout Frame **27a** to **g**, consider the graph of the sine function, Fig. IV.

    a Write the coordinates of the point P_1 as an ordered pair of real numbers.

    b Draw the tangent line to the graph at the point P_1, and find its slope.

    c Write an ordered pair of real numbers, the first coordinate of which is the abscissa of the point P_1 and the second coordinate of which is the slope of the tangent line at P_1.

    d Write an ordered pair of real numbers, the first coordinate of which is the abscissa of the point P_2 and the second of which is the slope of the tangent line at P_2.

20 It is indeed. For negative values, use $\cos(-x) = \cos x$, and for large values use $\cos x = -\cos(\pi - x)$ or $\cos x = \cos(2\pi - x)$.

21 It is. Since $\ln x$ is defined only when x is positive, there are no points on the graph on or to the left of the y axis.

22 It is.

23 They are the indicated graphs.

24 They are the graphs of the indicated functions.

25 For x negative we need apply $1/(-x) = -(1/x)$. Note, since $1/0$ is not a number, that 0 is not in the domain of the function. It is the graph of the reciprocal function.

26 We need distinguish between the number 2 and the *constant function* 2, i.e., the function f defined by the formula $f(x) = 2$. Here, $f(0) = 2$, $f(1) = 2, f(-2) = 2$. Note that the graph of each constant function is a horizontal line. The function x is called the *identity function:* it is the function g defined by $g(x) = x$; thus $g(1) = 1$, $g(0) = 0$, $g(-3) = -3$. The graph of this function is the line passing through the origin having $\pi/4$ (45°) as its angle of inclination.

27 **a** (0,0). The first coordinate is called the *abscissa* of the point, and the second coordinate is called its *ordinate*.

   b Its slope is 1. Your answer need only approximate this.

   c (0,1). See Frame **27b**.

   d (0.8, 0.7).

e Follow the instructions of Frame **27d** at the points P_3, P_4, . . . , P_9.

f On a second coordinate system, prepared to the same scale as Fig. IV, plot the points (ordered pairs of real numbers) obtained in Frame **27c** to **e**, then connect these points by a smooth curve.

g Compare the curve of Frame **27f** with the curves of Figs. I to VII.

28 Throughout Frame **28a** to **c**, consider the graph of the cosine curve, Fig. V.

a Write an ordered pair of real numbers, the first coordinate of which is the abscissa of the point P_1 and the second coordinate of which is the slope of the tangent line to the graph of the cosine function at the point P_1.

b Follow the instructions of Frame **28a** at the points P_2, P_3, . . . , P_9.

c On a second coordinate system, prepared to the same scale as Fig. V, plot the points (ordered pairs of real numbers) obtained in Frame **28a** and **b**, then connect these points by a smooth curve. Finally, compare this slope curve with the curves of Figs. I to VII.

29 Throughout Frame **29a** to **c**, consider the graph of the logarithmic function, Fig. VI.

a Write an ordered pair of real numbers, the first coordinate of which is the abscissa of the point P_1 and the second coordinate of which is the slope of the tangent line to the graph of the logarithmic function at the point P_1.

b Follow the instructions of Frame **29a** at the points P_2, P_3, . . . , P_7.

e   At P_3: $(1.6, 0)$; at P_4: $(2.8, -0.94)$; at P_5: $(3.1, -1)$; at P_6: $(4, -0.65)$; at P_7: $(4.7, 0)$; at P_8: $(5.5, 0.7)$; at P_9: $(6.3, 1)$.

f   This curve is called the *slope curve* of the sine function.

g   The slope curve of the sine function is precisely the graph of the cosine curve of Fig. V.   Thus *the slope curve of the sine function is the graph of the cosine function*.   In general the slope curve of a function is the graph of another function, called the *derivative* of the first function.   We designate the derivative of a function f by the symbol $D_x f$.   We have indicated in Frame **27a** to **g** that $D_x \sin x = \cos x$.   The student must understand that we have merely provided a plausible intuitive argument that the slope curve of the sine function is the graph of the cosine function.   It is by no means a *proof* of this result.   Your calculus course will include a more precise definition of the concept of a derivative and a more precise proof of the formula $D_x \sin x = \cos x$.   This remark extends to *all* the geometric demonstrations included in this chapter.

28   **a** $(0,0)$.

    b   At P_1: $(0,0)$; at P_2: $(0.8, -0.7)$; at P_3: $(1.6, -1)$; at P_4: $(2.8, -0.3)$; at P_5: $(3.1, 0)$; at P_6: $(4, 0.75)$; at P_7: $(4.7, 1)$; at P_8: $(5.5, 0.7)$; at P_9: $(6.3, 0)$.   Your answers need only approximate these.

    c   The slope curve is *related* to the sine curve in Fig. IV.   Actually it is the *reflection* of the sine curve about the x axis and is the graph of the *negative* of the sine function.   Thus the slope curve of the cosine function is the graph of the negative of the sine function.   Symbolically we write this as $D_x \cos x = -(\sin x)$.   The student will soon be expected to memorize these results; namely, $D_x \sin x = \cos x$ and $D_x \cos x = -(\sin x)$.   These are read as "the derivative of the sine function is the cosine function" and "the derivative of the cosine function is the negative of the sine function."

29   **a** $(0.2, 5)$.

    b   At P_2: $(0.4, 2.5)$; at P_3: $(0.6, 1.7)$; at P_4: $(1,1)$; at P_5: $(2, 0.5)$; at P_6: $(4, 0.25)$; at P_7: $(7, 0.14)$.

c On a second coordinate system prepared to the same scale as Fig. VI, plot the points obtained in Frame **29a** and **b**, then connect these points by a smooth curve and compare this slope curve with the curves of Figs. I to VII.

30 Consider the graph of the exponential function e^x, Fig. VII. Select the points P_1, P_2, . . . , P_7 on this graph, and for each point write an ordered pair of real numbers, the first coordinate of which is the abscissa of the point and the second coordinate of which is the slope of the tangent line to the graph of the exponential function at this point. Plot these ordered pairs (points) on a second coordinate system prepared to the same scale as Fig. VII and connect these points by a smooth curve. Finally, compare this curve with those of Figs. I to VII.

31 Construct the slope curve of the function x^3, Fig. III. Compare this with the curves in Figs. I to VII. (Follow the instructions of Frame **30** to construct the slope curve.)

32 Construct the slope curve of the function x^2, Fig. II. Finally, compare this with the curves in Figs. I to VII.

33 Construct the slope curve of the identity function x, Fig. I. Compare this with the curves of Figs. I to VII.

34 Construct the slope curve of the constant function 2. Compare this with the curves of Figs. I to VII. Do the same for the constant function 1; for the constant function 0.

35 From the results $D_x x^2 = 2x$ and $D_x x^3 = 3x^2$, can you guess $D_x x^4$? $D_x x^5$?

c The slope curve of the logarithmic function is half the graph of the reciprocal function, $1/x$, i.e., all the points of the graph having positive abscissas. We write $D_x \ln x = 1/x$, but since the $\ln x$ is defined only when x is positive, the formula applies only in this case. If the student would construct the graph of the function $\ln |x|$ which is defined for all numbers x, except 0, and construct the slope curve of this function, he would find that it coincided with the entire graph of the reciprocal function $D_x \ln |x| = 1/x$.

30 At P_1: $(-1, 0.37)$; at P_2: $(-0.5, 0.6)$; at P_3: $(0,1)$; at P_4: $(0.5, 1.6)$; at P_5: $(1, 2.7)$; at P_6: $(1.3, 3.7)$; at P_7: $(2, 7.4)$. This is an interesting result: the slope curve of the exponential function is itself the graph of the exponential function, $D_x e^x = e^x$. At this stage we have the following results which the student need memorize:

$$D_x \sin x = \cos x \qquad D_x \cos x = -(\sin x) \qquad D_x \ln |x| = 1/x \qquad D_x e^x = e^x.$$

31 The slope curve of the function x^3 is the graph of the function $3x^2$: $D_x x^3 = 3x^2$.

32 The slope curve of the function x^2 is the graph of the function $2x$: $D_x x^2 = 2x$.

33 The slope curve of the identity function x is the constant function 1: $D_x x = 1$.

34 The graph of each constant function is a horizontal line having slope 0. Thus the slope curve of any constant function is the constant zero function: $D_x k = 0$. The recent results which the student must commit to memory are:

$$D_x k = 0 \qquad D_x x = 1 \qquad D_x x^2 = 2x \qquad D_x x^3 = 3x^2.$$

35 $D_x x^4 = 4x^3$ and $D_x x^5 = 5x^4$. In fact we will apply this formula, even when the exponent is not a positive integer: $D_x x^a = ax^{a-1}$. Thus $D_x x^{\frac{3}{2}} = \frac{3}{2} x^{\frac{1}{2}}$.

36 The slope curve of a function is the graph of another function, called the *derivative* of the first function. Check to see if you have yet memorized the derivatives herein indicated:

$$D_x \sin x = ? \qquad D_x \cos x = ? \qquad D_x \ln x = ? \qquad D_x e^x = ?$$
$$D_x x^a = ? \qquad D_x x = ? \qquad D_x k = ?$$

We must repeat for emphasis that the purpose of this chapter was to provide an intuitive geometric definition of the derivative concept as well as plausible arguments for the derivative formulas appearing in Frame **36** above. A precise definition of the derivative concept and precise proofs of these formulas form a significant part of a course in calculus, but are not here included. Read, in particular, the first three paragraphs of the preface to this program.

36 $D_x \sin x = \cos x$ $D_x \cos x = -(\sin x)$ $D_x \ln x = 1/x$

$D_x e^x = e^x$ $D_x x^a = a x^{a-1}$ $D_x x = 1$ $D_x k = 0$

chapter 2

Technique of Differentiation

We assume the student has now completed the geometric derivation of the following derivative formulas and has committed these to memory:

$$D_x \sin x = \cos x \qquad D_x \cos x = -(\sin x) \qquad D_x \ln |x| = \frac{1}{x}$$
$$D_x e^x = e^x \qquad D_x x^a = ax^{a-1} \qquad D_x k = 0 \qquad D_x x = 1$$

More complex functions are obtained from these by the operations of addition, subtraction, multiplication, and division and by two additional operations called *composition* and *inversion*. We will soon exhibit, without proofs, theorems which relate these operations with the derivative. These theorems, stated more precisely and accompanied by proofs, will form a significant part of the student's course in the calculus. The first of these theorems follows. *The derivative of the sum of two functions is the sum of their derivatives; the derivative of the difference of two functions is the difference of their derivatives*

$$D_x(f + g) = (D_x f) + (D_x g) \qquad D_x(f - g) = (D_x f) - (D_x g)$$

1 $D_x(\sin x + \cos x) = ?$

2 $D_x(\sin x - \cos x) = ?$

3 $D_x(x^3 + 5) = ?$

4 $D_x(\ln |x| + x^7) = ?$

5 $D_x(e^x - x^e) = ?$

6 $D_x(\ln |x| + x^{-1}) = ?$

7 $D_x(x^{\frac{2}{3}} + 7) = ?$

1 $\cos x - \sin x$. The function defined by the formula $\sin x + \cos x$ is the sum of two functions $\sin x$ and $\cos x$. Since $D_x \sin x = \cos x$ and $D_x \cos x = -(\sin x)$,

$$D_x(\sin x + \cos x) = \cos x + (-\sin x) = \cos x - \sin x.$$

2 $\cos x + \sin x$. The function defined by the formula $\sin x - \cos x$ is the *difference* of two functions $\sin x$ and $\cos x$. Since $D_x \sin x = \cos x$ and $D_x \cos x = -\sin x$,

$$D_x(\sin x - \cos x) = D_x \sin x - D_x \cos x$$
$$= \cos x - (-\sin x) = \cos x + \sin x.$$

3 $3x^2 + 0 = 3x^2$. That $D_x x^3 = 3x^2$ follows from the formula $D_x x^a = ax^{a-1}$ by replacing a by 3.

4 $1/x + 7x^6$

5 $e^x - ex^{e-1}$. The number e is approximately $2.71828 \ldots$. That $D_x x^e = ex^{e-1}$ follows from the formula $D_x x^a = ax^{a-1}$ by replacing a by the constant e. The student must distinguish the *exponential* function e^x from the *power* functions x^a, in that the *variable* x appears as the *exponent* in the exponential function but as the *base* in a power function.

6 $\dfrac{1}{x} + (-1)x^{-2}$. Since $x^{-2} = \dfrac{1}{x^2}$, this can be written in simplified form as $\dfrac{x-1}{x^2}$.

7 $\frac{2}{3}x^{-\frac{1}{3}} + 0 = \frac{2}{3}x^{-\frac{1}{3}}$

8   **a**   Let $f = 2$, $g = x$. Then $f \cdot g = 2 \cdot x = 2x = x + x$. Compute $D_x f$, $D_x g$, $D_x (f \cdot g)$.

     b   Does $D_x (f \cdot g)$ equal $(D_x f) \cdot (D_x g)$ for the functions defined in Frame **8a**?

9   **a**   Let $f = x$, $g = x$. Then $f \cdot g = x \cdot x = x^2$. Compute $D_x f$, $D_x g$, $D_x (f \cdot g)$.

     b   Does $D_x (f \cdot g) = (D_x f) \cdot (D_x g)$ for the functions defined in Frame **9a**?

The derivative of the product of two functions is the sum of the products of each function by the derivative of the other

$$D_x(f \cdot g) = f \cdot (D_x g) + g \cdot (D_x f)$$

---

10 $D_x(\sin x \cdot \cos x) = ?$

11 $D_x(x^2 \cdot e^x) = ?$

12 $D_t(t \cdot \sin t) = ?$

13 $D_u(\sqrt{u} \cdot \ln u) = ?$

14 $D_x(3 \cdot x^{\frac{1}{3}}) = ?$

15 $D_t(k \cdot \sin t) = ?$

8 a $D_x f = D_x 2 = 0 \qquad D_x g = D_x x = 1$
$D_x(f \cdot g) = D_x(x + x) = D_x x + D_x x = 1 + 1 = 2$

b No! By Frame **8a**, $D_x(f \cdot g) = 2$ and $(D_x f) \cdot (D_x g) = 0 \cdot 1 = 0$. From this example we see that we *cannot* in general expect the derivative of the product of two functions to be the product of their derivatives.

9 a $D_x f = D_x x = 1 \qquad D_x g = D_x x = 1 \qquad D_x(f \cdot g) = D_x x^2 = 2x$

b No. By Frame **9a**, $D_x(f \cdot g) = 2x$ and $(D_x f) \cdot (D_x g) = 1 \cdot 1 = 1$. Again we see that we cannot expect the derivative of the product of the two functions to be the product of their derivatives.

10 $D_x(\sin x \cos x) = \sin x (D_x \cos x) + \cos x (D_x \sin x)$
$$= \sin x(-\sin x) + \cos x \cos x = \cos^2 x - \sin^2 x$$

Thus to find the derivative of the product of two functions, multiply the first function (*not its derivative*) by the derivative of the second function, then multiply the second function by the derivative of the first, and finally add these products.

11 $D_x(x^2 \cdot e^x) = x^2 D_x e^x + e^x D_x x^2 = x^2 e^x + e^x 2x$. This can be written in equivalent algebraic form as $xe^x(x + 2)$. If you wrote $D_x e^x = xe^{x-1}$, you were confusing the exponential function with the power function.

12 $t \cdot \cos t + \sin t$. Any letter may be used as the variable element of the domain of a function.

13 $u^{\frac{1}{2}} \cdot \dfrac{1}{u} + (\ln u)\frac{1}{2}u^{-\frac{1}{2}}$. Show that this is algebraically equivalent to $\dfrac{2 + \ln u}{2 \sqrt{u}}$. Since functions $\sqrt{u}$ and $\ln u$ are both defined only when u is positive, this derivative formula obtains only when u is positive.

14 $3 \cdot \frac{1}{3}x^{-\frac{2}{3}} + x^{\frac{1}{3}} \cdot 0 = 3 \cdot \frac{1}{3}x^{-\frac{2}{3}}$. Note that this answer is $3 \cdot D_x x^{\frac{1}{3}}$.

15 $k \cos t$. Note that this answer is $kD_t \sin t$. Can you guess, from the last two questions, a special product formula for the derivative of a constant function times another function: $D_x(k \cdot f)$?

16 Apply the product formula, then simplify, to derive a special formula for $D_x(k \cdot f) = ?$

The derivative of a constant times a function is the constant times the derivative of the function

$$D_x(k \cdot f) = k \cdot D_x f$$

---

17 $D_x(3x^2) = ?$ Do this two ways; first, apply the general product formula, then apply the special formula stated above.

18 $D_x(3x^2 \cdot \sin x) = ?$ Note that the product of three functions can be written as the product of two functions: $3 \cdot x^2 \cdot \sin x = (3x^2) \cdot \sin x$.

19 Write $e^{2x} = e^x \cdot e^x$ and find $D_x(e^{2x})$.

20 $D_x(x^3 + 5x^2 - 7) = ?$ Convince yourself that the formula for the derivative of a sum or difference extends to any number of terms.

21 $D_x(x \cdot \sin x - x^2 \cdot \ln |x| + 7x^{-\frac{1}{3}}) = ?$

22 a Let $f = x^3$, $g = x$. Then, at least when $x \neq 0$, $f/g = x^3/x = x^2$. Find $D_x f$, $D_x g$, and $D_x(f/g)$.

b Is $D_x(f/g) = D_x f / D_x g$ for the functions defined in Frame **22a**?

The Derivative of the Quotient of Two Functions

$$D_x \frac{f}{g} = \frac{g(D_x f) - f(D_x g)}{g^2}$$

Since quotients are not commutative, i.e., $f/g \neq g/f$, the formula for the derivative of a quotient is not symmetric in f and g. The expression on the right may be read: the denominator (of f/g) times the derivative of the numerator minus the numerator times the derivative of the denominator, all divided by the square of the denominator. Of course g^2 means $g \cdot g$.

---

16 $D_x(k \cdot f) = k \cdot (D_x f) + f \cdot (D_x k) = k \cdot (D_x f) + f \cdot 0 = k \cdot (D_x f)$. Thus *the derivative of a constant (function) times a function is the constant times the derivative of the function*: $D_x(k \cdot f) = k \cdot (D_x f)$.

17 $D_x(3x^2) = 3 \cdot D_x(x^2) + x^2(D_x 3) = 3 \cdot 2x + x^2 \cdot 0 = 6x$
$D_x(3x^2) = 3 \cdot D_x(x^2) = 3(2x) = 6x$

18 $3x^2 \cdot \cos x + (\sin x)6x$. It is important to emphasize that *the derivative of a function is a function*.

19 $D_x e^{2x} = D_x(e^x e^x) = e^x D_x e^x + e^x D_x e^x = e^x e^x + e^x e^x = 2e^{2x}$. Note that $D_x e^{2x} \neq e^{2x}$.

20 $3x^2 + 10x$

21 $x \cdot \cos x + \sin x - \left[x^2 \dfrac{1}{x} + (\ln |x|)2x \right] + 7(-\frac{1}{3}x^{-\frac{4}{3}})$. Have you been careful with the use of parentheses? Note that $-a + b \neq -(a + b)$ and $7 - \frac{1}{3}f$ is entirely different from $7(-\frac{1}{3}f)$.

22 **a** $D_x f = D_x x^3 = 3x^2$ $\qquad D_x g = D_x x = 1 \qquad D_x \dfrac{f}{g} = D_x x^2 = 2x$

b No. $D_x \dfrac{f}{g} = 2x$ and $\dfrac{D_x f}{D_x g} = \dfrac{3x^2}{1} = 3x^2$. From this example we can see that the derivative of the quotient of two functions need *not* be the quotient of their derivatives. We have instead the formula exhibited in the following remark frame, which the student should memorize.

23 a Let $f = x^3$, $g = x$. Then $f/g = x^2$. Find $D_x f$, $D_x g$, and $D_x(f/g)$.

b Apply Frame **23a** to verify the formula for the derivative of a quotient given above.

24 $D_x(x/\sin x) = ?$ (Assume, of course, $\sin x \neq 0$, i.e., that no integral multiple of π is in the domain of the function considered.)

25 The tangent function can be written as the quotient of the sine and cosine functions (on a suitably restricted domain): $\tan x = \dfrac{\sin x}{\cos x}$. Thus $D_x \tan x = D_x \dfrac{\sin x}{\cos x}$. Derive a formula for $D_x \tan x$.

26 Derive a formula for $D_x \cot x = D_x \dfrac{\cos x}{\sin x}$.

27 Derive a formula for $D_x \sec x$. The secant function can be written as $1/\cos x$.

28 Derive a formula for $D_x \csc x$.

We have now derived formulas for the derivatives of all six trigonometric functions. It is necessary that the student commit these also to memory since the technique of *integration* which appears in the sequel is predicated on the recognition of type forms, and these type forms are precisely the formulas for the derivatives of the elementary functions. To facilitate memorization we list:

$$D_x \sin x = \cos x \qquad D_x \tan x = \sec^2 x \qquad D_x \sec x = \sec x \tan x$$
$$D_x \cos x = -\sin x \qquad D_x \cot x = -\csc^2 x \qquad D_x \csc x = -\csc x \cot x$$

Note the cofunctional relationships that appear.

29 $D_x(5 \tan x) = ?$

30 $D_x(x^5 \sec x) = ?$

31 $D_x(\ln x - \cot x) = ?$

23 a $D_x f = D_x x^3 = 3x^2$ $D_x g = D_x x = 1$ $D_x \dfrac{f}{g} = D_x x^2 = 2x$

b $D_x \dfrac{f}{g} = D_x x^2 = 2x$

$$\frac{g(D_x f) - f(D_x g)}{g^2} = \frac{x \cdot 3x^2 - x^3 \cdot 1}{x^2} = \frac{2x^3}{x^2} = 2x$$

24 $\dfrac{\sin x - x \cdot \cos x}{\sin^2 x}$. If you obtained $\dfrac{x \cdot \cos x - \sin x}{\cos^2 x}$ you interchanged the role of numerator and denominator in the quotient formula.

25 $\sec^2 x$. You may have correctly obtained $(\cos^2 x + \sin^2 x)/\cos^2 x$ or $1/\cos^2 x$ as your answer. These are all equivalent, since $\cos^2 x + \sin^2 x = 1$ and $\sec x = 1/\cos x$. Here is another formula to memorize:

$D_x \tan x = \sec^2 x.$

26 $-\csc^2 x$. The following are equivalent answers:

$$\frac{-\sin^2 x - \cos^2 x}{\sin^2 x} \qquad \frac{-1}{\sin^2 x}.$$

Thus $D_x \cot x = -\csc^2 x$. This formula should also be committed to memory.

27 $\sec x \tan x$. An equivalent correct answer is $\dfrac{\sin x}{\cos^2 x}$. Thus

$D_x \sec x = \sec x \tan x.$

28 $D_x \csc x = -\csc x \cot x$

29 $D_x(5 \tan x) = 5 \sec^2 x$

30 $x^5 \sec x \tan x + (\sec x)5x^4$

31 $\dfrac{1}{x} - (-\csc^2 x) = \dfrac{1}{x} + \csc^2 x$

32 $D_t(e^t \csc t) = ?$

33 $D_u \dfrac{\ln u}{\sin u} = ?$

34 $D_x \dfrac{\tan x}{x^2} = ?$

35 $D_t \dfrac{\csc t}{5} = ?$

36 $D_x \dfrac{\cot x}{e^x} = ?$

37 $D_u(3e^u \cos u) = ?$

38 $D_x(\sec x + \tan x) = ?$

39 $D_x \dfrac{\ln x}{\csc x} = ?$

40 $D_u \dfrac{\cot u}{3} = ?$

41 $D_x \sin^2 x = ?$

42 $D_x(\sin^2 x + \cos^2 x) = ?$

Composition of Two Functions Consider the function $\sin\left(\dfrac{\pi}{2} + x\right)$. It is *not* the *product* of two functions but is instead the sine function of the $\left(\dfrac{\pi}{2} + x\right)$ function, i.e., a function *of* a function. This process of forming a new function $\sin\left(\dfrac{\pi}{2} + x\right)$ from simpler functions $\sin x$ and $\dfrac{\pi}{2} + x$ is called *composition*. In general, given two functions f and g, defined on suitable domains, then the composition of the two functions is defined by the for-

32 $e^t(-\csc t \cot t) + (\csc t)e^t$

33 $\dfrac{(\sin u)(1/u) - (\ln u)\cos u}{\sin^2 u}$

34 $\dfrac{x^2 \sec^2 x - (\tan x)2x}{x^4}$

35 $\dfrac{5(-\csc t \cot t) - (\csc t)0}{25}$.   However if we write $\dfrac{\csc t}{5} = \dfrac{1}{5}\csc t$, we have simply

$$D_t \frac{\csc t}{5} = D_t \frac{1}{5}\csc t = \frac{1}{5}(-\csc t \cot t).$$

36 $\dfrac{e^x(-\csc^2 x) - (\cot x)e^x}{e^{2x}}$.   Note $(e^x)^2 = e^{2x}$.

37 $3e^u(-\sin u) + (\cos u)3e^u$

38 $\sec x \tan x + \sec^2 x$

39 $\dfrac{\csc x(1/x) - \ln x(-\csc x \cdot \cot x)}{\csc^2 x}$

40 $D_u \dfrac{\cot u}{3} = D_u(\tfrac{1}{3}\cot u) = \tfrac{1}{3}(-\csc^2 u)$

41 $D_x \sin^2 x = D_x(\sin x \sin x) = \sin x \cos x + \sin x \cos x$
$$= 2\sin x \cos x$$

42   Instead of writing $\sin^2 x + \cos^2 x = \sin x \sin x + \cos x \cos x$ and then finding the derivative, the following trickery can be applied: $D_x(\sin^2 x + \cos^2 x) = D_x 1 = 0.$

mula $f[g(x)]$.   It is convenient to use the following notation for this concept: $f(u)|^{u=g(x)} = f[g(x)]$.   The notation $f(u)|^{u=g(x)}$ is particularly useful when both f and g are defined by formulas.   For example, $\sin u|^{u=(\pi/2)-x}$ is the function which at x has the value $\sin\left(\dfrac{\pi}{2} - x\right)$.

43 Write a formula for $\sin u|^{u=2x}$.

44 Write a formula for $\ln u|^{u=x^2}$.

45 Write a formula for $\tan u|^{u=\frac{\pi}{2}-2x}$.

46 Write a formula for $e^u|^{u=\tan x}$.

47 Write a formula for $e^u|^{u=x^3}$.

48 Write a formula for $e^u|^{u=\ln x}$.

49 Write a formula for $u^2|^{u=\sin x}$.

50 Write a formula for $u^2|^{u=e^x}$.

51 Write a formula for $\sqrt{u}|^{u=e^x}$.

52 Write a formula for $u^3|^{u=x^2-2x+5}$.

53 Write a formula for $u^2 - 2u + 5|^{u=\sin x}$.

54 Write a formula for $u^2 - 2u + 5|^{u=x^2+1}$.

55 Write $\cos 2x$ in the form $f(u)|^{u=g(x)}$.

56 Write $\sin\left(\dfrac{\pi}{2} - x\right)$ in the form $f(u)|^{u=g(x)}$.

57 Write $\sin x^2$ in the form $f(u)|^{u=g(x)}$.

58 Write $\sin^2 x$ in the form $f(u)|^{u=g(x)}$.

43 $\sin u|^{u=2x} = \sin 2x$. Operationally, the symbol $f(u)|^{u=g(x)}$ instructs one to replace the variable u, in the formula for $f(u)$, by the formula for $g(x)$.

44 $\ln u|^{u=x^2} = \ln x^2$. Of course, if you wish, the theory of logarithms permits this last expression to be written as $2(\ln x)$.

45 $\tan u|^{u=(\pi/2)-2x} = \tan\left(\dfrac{\pi}{2} - 2x\right) = \cot 2x$

46 $e^u|^{u=\tan x} = e^{\tan x}$

47 $e^u|^{u=x^3} = e^{x^3}$

48 $e^u|^{u=\ln x} = e^{\ln x}$. Since, by definition, $\ln x = \log_e x$ is the power to which the base must be raised to attain x, $e^{\ln x} = x$. Two functions f and g for which $f(u)|^{u=g(x)}$ equals the identity function x are called *inverse functions*. Thus the exponential and logarithmic functions are inverse functions.

49 $u^2|^{u=\sin x} = (\sin x)^2 = \sin^2 x$. The symbol $\sin^2 x$ means $(\sin x)^2$ and is employed to avoid the use of parentheses.

50 $u^2|^{u=e^x} = (e^x)^2 = e^{2x}$

51 $\sqrt{u}|^{u=e^x} = \sqrt{e^x}$. If you wish, this last expression can be written as a power: $(e^x)^{\frac{1}{2}} = e^{x/2}$.

52 $u^3|^{u=x^2-2x+5} = (x^2 - 2x + 5)^3$

53 $(\sin x)^2 - 2(\sin x) + 5 = \sin^2 x - 2\sin x + 5$

54 $(x^2 + 1)^2 - 2(x^2 + 1) + 5$. This can be written as a polynomial in standard form: $x^4 + 4$.

55 $\cos 2x = \cos u|^{u=2x}$

56 $\sin\left(\dfrac{\pi}{2} - x\right) = \sin u|^{u=(\pi/2)-x}$

57 $\sin x^2 = \sin u|^{u=x^2}$

58 $\sin^2 x = (\sin x)^2 = u^2|^{u=\sin x}$

59 Write e^{-x} in the form $f(u)|_{u=g(x)}$.

60 Write $(x^2 + 1)^3 + 5(x^2 + 1) - 2$ in the form $f(u)|_{u=g(x)}$.

61 Write $(x^2 + 1)^3 - \sin(x^2 + 1) + \sqrt{x^2 + 1}$ in the form $f(u)|_{u=g(x)}$.

The formula for the derivative of the composition of two functions is called the *chain rule*. If f and g are two functions and if $D_x f = f'$ and $D_x g = g'$, then $D_x[g(x)] = f'[g(x)] \cdot g'(x)$. It is easier to apply the chain rule when using the special notation for composition:

$$D_x[f(u)|_{u=g(x)}] = f'(u) \cdot g'(x)|_{u=g(x)}$$

What does it say operationally?   To take the derivative of the composition $f(u)|_{u=g(x)}$, first find the derivative $f'(u)$ of $f(u)$ and multiply this by the derivative $g'(x)$ of $g(x)$, *then* replace u by $g(x)$.

---

62 $D_x (\sin u|_{u=g(x)}) = ?$

63 $D_x \sin 2x = ?$

64 $D_x e^{g(x)} = ?$

65 $D_x e^{-x} = ?$

66 $D_x \cos g(x) = ?$

67 $D_x \cos x^2 = ?$

68 $D_x \tan g(x) = ?$

69 $D_x \cot \ln x = ?$

70 $D_x \sec e^x = ?$

71 $D_x \ln g(x) = ?$

72 $D_x \sqrt{\sin x} = ?$

59 $e^{-x} = e^u\big|_{u=-x}$

60 $(x^2 + 1)^3 + 5(x^2 + 1) - 2 = u^3 + 5u - 2\big|_{u=x^2+1}$

61 $(x^2 + 1)^3 - \sin(x^2 + 1) + \sqrt{x^2 + 1} = (u^3 - \sin u + \sqrt{u})\big|_{u=x^2+1}$

62 $D_x(\sin u\big|_{u=g(x)}) = \cos u \cdot g'(x)\big|_{u=g(x)} = \cos[g(x)] \cdot g'(x)$. Here, with $f(u) = \sin u$, $f'(u) = \cos u$, and the result follows from the chain rule.

63 $D_x \sin 2x = D_x(\sin u\big|_{u=2x}) = \cos u \cdot 2\big|_{u=2x} = 2\cos 2x$. The factor 2 is the factor $g'(x)$ appearing in the chain rule.

64 $D_x e^{g(x)} = D_x(e^u\big|_{u=g(x)}) = e^u g'(x)\big|_{u=g(x)} = e^{g(x)}g'(x)$. We first write $e^{g(x)}$ in the form $f(u)\big|_{u=g(x)}$, where $f(u) = e^u$. Then $f'(u) = e^u$, and the chain rule is applied.

65 $D_x e^{-x} = D_x(e^u\big|_{u=-x}) = e^u(-1)\big|_{u=-x} = -e^{-x}$

66 $D_x \cos g(x) = D_x(\cos u\big|_{u=g(x)}) = -\sin u \cdot g'(x)\big|_{u=g(x)} = -\sin[g(x)] \cdot g'(x)$

67 $D_x \cos x^2 = D_x(\cos u\big|_{u=x^2}) = -\sin u \cdot 2x\big|_{u=x^2} = -2x\sin x^2$

68 $D_x \tan g(x) = D_x(\tan u\big|_{u=g(x)}) = \sec^2 u \cdot g'(x)\big|_{u=g(x)} = \sec^2[g(x)] \cdot g'(x)$

69 $D_x \cot \ln x = D_x(\cot u\big|_{u=\ln x}) = -\csc^2 u \cdot \dfrac{1}{x}\bigg|_{u=\ln x} = \dfrac{-\csc^2(\ln x)}{x}$

70 $D_x \sec e^x = D_x(\sec u\big|_{u=e^x}) = \sec u \cdot \tan u \cdot e^x\big|_{u=e^x} = \sec e^x \tan e^x \cdot e^x$

71 $D_x \ln g(x) = D_x(\ln u\big|_{u=g(x)}) = \dfrac{1}{u} g'(x)\big|_{u=g(x)} = \dfrac{g'(x)}{g(x)}$

72 $D_x \sqrt{\sin x} = D_x(u^{\frac{1}{2}}\big|_{u=\sin x}) = \tfrac{1}{2}u^{-\frac{1}{2}}\cos x\big|_{u=\sin x} = \dfrac{\cos x}{2\sqrt{\sin x}}$

73 $D_x \sqrt{x^2 + 9} = ?$

74 We now ask the student to repeat Frames **63** to **73**, but this time without writing down the auxiliary variable u. He must think of each problem as the composition of two functions and apply the chain rule.

a $D_x \sin 2x = ?$ **g** $D_x \cot \ln x = ?$

b $D_x e^{g(x)} = ?$ **h** $D_x \sec e^x = ?$

c $D_x e^{-x} = ?$ **i** $D_x \ln g(x) = ?$

d $D_x \cos g(x) = ?$ **j** $D_x \sqrt{\sin x} = ?$

e $D_x \cos x^2 = ?$ **k** $D_x \sqrt{x^2 + 9} = ?$

f $D_x \tan g(x) = ?$

75 $D_x[g(x)]^a = ?$

76 $D_x \sin^3 x = ?$ Note, $\sin^3 x = (\sin x)^3$.

77 $D_x \sqrt{(\cos x) + 7} = ?$

78 $D_x (\ln x)^{-1} = ?$

79 $D_x (x^3 - 5x^2 + 2x - 5)^{-\frac{1}{3}} = ?$

80 $D_x \sin (x^3 - 5x^2 + 2x - 5) = ?$

81 $D_x \sin \ln x = ?$

82 $D_x \sin^5 x = ?$

83 Find $D_x \sin \dfrac{1 - x}{x}$.

73 $D_x \sqrt{x^2 + 9} = D_x(u^{\frac{1}{2}}|_{u=x^2+9}) = \frac{1}{2}u^{-\frac{1}{2}} \cdot 2x|_{u=x^2+9} = \dfrac{x}{\sqrt{x^2 + 9}}$

74 **a** $D_x \sin 2x = \cos 2x \cdot 2$ **g** $D_x \cot (\ln x) = -\csc^2 (\ln x) \dfrac{1}{x}$

b $D_x e^{g(x)} = e^{g(x)} g'(x)$ **h** $D_x \sec e^x = \sec e^x \cdot \tan e^x \cdot e^x$

c $D_x e^{-x} = e^{-x}(-1)$ **i** $D_x \ln g(x) = \dfrac{1}{g(x)} g'(x)$

d $D_x \cos g(x) = -\sin [g(x)] \cdot g'(x)$ **j** $D_x(\sin x)^{\frac{1}{2}} = \frac{1}{2}(\sin x)^{-\frac{1}{2}} \cdot \cos x$

e $D_x \cos x^2 = -\sin x^2 \cdot 2x$ **k** $D_x(x^2 + 9)^{\frac{1}{2}} = \frac{1}{2}(x^2 + 9)^{-\frac{1}{2}} \cdot 2x$

f $D_x \tan g(x) = \sec^2 g(x) \cdot g'(x)$

75 $D_x[g(x)]^a = D_x(u^a|_{u=g(x)}) = a \cdot u^{a-1}g'(x)|_{u=g(x)} = a[g(x)]^{a-1}g'(x)$, or simply $D_x[g(x)]^a = a[g(x)]^{a-1}g'(x)$.

76 $D_x(\sin x)^3 = 3(\sin x)^2 \cos x$

77 $D_x(\cos x + 7)^{\frac{1}{2}} = \frac{1}{2}(\cos x + 7)^{-\frac{1}{2}}(-\sin x)$

78 $D_x(\ln x)^{-1} = -1(\ln x)^{-2} \dfrac{1}{x}$

79 $D_x(x^3 - 5x^2 + 2x - 5)^{-\frac{1}{3}} = -\frac{1}{3}(x^3 - 5x^2 + 2x - 5)^{-\frac{4}{3}}(3x^2 - 10x + 2)$. Did you omit the parentheses about $3x^2 - 10x + 2$? Without these parentheses, the expression means something quite different—and incorrect.

80 $D_x \sin (x^3 - 5x^2 + 2x - 5) = [\cos (x^3 - 5x^2 + 2x - 5)](3x^2 - 10x + 2)$

81 $D_x \sin \ln x = \cos \ln x \cdot D_x \ln x = \cos \ln x \cdot 1/x$

82 Recognize the function $\sin^5 x$ as $(\sin x)^5$. Thus

$D_x \sin^5 x = D_x(\sin x)^5 = 5(\sin x)^4 D_x(\sin x) = 5 \sin^4 x \cos x$.

83 $D_x \sin \dfrac{1 - x}{x} = \cos \dfrac{1 - x}{x} D_x \dfrac{1 - x}{x} = \left(\cos \dfrac{1 - x}{x}\right)\left(-\dfrac{1}{x^2}\right)$. The last factor is the derivative of the quotient $\dfrac{1 - x}{x}$.

84 Find $D_x \cos x \sin 2x$.

85 Find $D_x \sin \sqrt{x}$.

86 Find $D_x \sin \sqrt{2x + 1}$.

87 Find $D_x \dfrac{\sin 2bx}{4b}$. Think of b as a given constant.

88 Find $D_x \cos x^3$.

89 Find $D_x \cos^3 x$.

90 Find $D_x \cos (x^2 - 5x)$.

91 Find $D_x \sqrt{\cos \dfrac{x}{2}}$.

84 The function $\cos x \sin 2x$ is a *product*, not a composition. Thus

$$D_x \cos x \sin 2x = \cos x \; D_x \sin 2x + \sin 2x \cdot D_x \cos x$$
$$= \cos x \cdot \cos 2x \cdot \underline{2} + \sin 2x \cdot (-\sin x).$$

Did you omit the underlined factor 2 or the parentheses about $(-\sin x)$?

85 $D_x \sin \sqrt{x} = D_x \sin x^{\frac{1}{2}} = (\cos x^{\frac{1}{2}})\frac{1}{2}x^{-\frac{1}{2}} = \dfrac{\cos \sqrt{x}}{2\sqrt{x}}$

86 $D_x \sin \sqrt{2x+1} = D_x \sin [(2x+1)^{\frac{1}{2}}]$
$$= \cos [(2x+1)^{\frac{1}{2}}] \cdot D_x[(2x+1)^{\frac{1}{2}}]$$
$$= \cos \sqrt{2x+1} \cdot \tfrac{1}{2}(2x+1)^{-\frac{1}{2}} \cdot 2 = \dfrac{\cos \sqrt{2x+1}}{\sqrt{2x+1}}$$

Note that the chain rule is applied twice; once on sin ( ) and once on $(2x+1)^{\frac{1}{2}}$. This is necessary since the function $\sin \sqrt{2x+1}$ is the sine function of the square root function of the $2x+1$ function.

87 The given function is a quotient. Thus its derivative is given by

$$\frac{4bD_x \sin (2bx) - \sin (2bx) \cdot D_x 4b}{16b^2} = \frac{4b \cos (2bx) \cdot 2b - 0}{16b^2} = \frac{\cos (2bx)}{2}$$

Since the denominator of the function $\dfrac{\sin (2bx)}{4b}$ is a constant, it would have been easier to write as the product $\dfrac{1}{4b} \sin (2bx)$, and since $\dfrac{1}{4b}$ is a constant, the derivative can be obtained more simply as

$$\frac{1}{4b} D_x \sin (2bx) = \frac{1}{4b} \cos (2bx) \cdot 2b.$$

88 $D_x \cos x^3 = -(\sin x^3) \cdot 3x^2$

89 $D_x \cos^3 x = D_x(\cos x)^3 = 3(\cos x)^2(-\sin x) = -3(\sin x)(\cos^2 x)$

90 $D_x \cos (x^2 - 5x) = -\sin (x^2 - 5x) \cdot (2x - 5)$
$$= (5 - 2x) \sin (x^2 - 5x)$$

91 $D_x \left(\cos \dfrac{x}{2}\right)^{\frac{1}{2}} = \dfrac{1}{2}\left(\cos \dfrac{x}{2}\right)^{-\frac{1}{2}} D_x \cos \dfrac{x}{2} = \dfrac{1}{2}\left(\cos \dfrac{x}{2}\right)^{-\frac{1}{2}}\left(-\sin \dfrac{x}{2}\right)\dfrac{1}{2}$
$$= \frac{-\sin (x/2)}{4\sqrt{\cos (x/2)}}$$

92 Find $D_x \cos \sqrt{\dfrac{x}{2}}$.

93 **a** $D_x \sin (3x^2) = \, ?$

  b $D_x \sin (3x)^2 = \, ?$

  c $D_x \sin^2 3x = \, ?$

Two functions f and g, defined on suitable domains, are called *inverse functions* if their composition $f[g(x)]$ is the identity function x on the domain of g, i.e., if $f(u)\big|^{u=g(x)} = x$. A theorem on inverse functions states that if f has a nonzero derivative, then g has a derivative. We now introduce some inverse trigonometric functions and apply the stated theorem and the chain rule to find their derivatives.

---

94 We recall from trigonometry that if $-1 \leq x \leq 1$ and $u = \arcsin x$, then $-\dfrac{\pi}{2} \leq u \leq \dfrac{\pi}{2}$ and $\sin u = x$. Show that, under these conditions, $\cos u = \sqrt{1 - x^2}$.

95 By taking derivatives of both sides of the equation $\sin u\big|^{u=\arcsin x} = x$, find a formula giving the derivative of the arcsin function.

96 Again from trigonometry, if $-1 \leq x \leq 1$ and $u = \arccos x$, then $0 \leq u \leq \pi$ and $\cos u = x$. Show that, under these conditions, $\sin u = \sqrt{1 - x^2}$.

97 By taking the derivatives of both sides of the equation $\cos u\big|^{u=\arccos x} = x$, find a formula giving the derivative of the arccos function.

98 If $u = \arctan x$, then $\tan u = x$. Show that $\sec^2 u = 1 + x^2$.

99 Start with the inverse function property $\tan u\big|^{u=\arctan x} = x$ and derive a formula giving the derivative of the arctan function.

92 $-\sin\sqrt{\dfrac{x}{2}} \cdot \dfrac{1}{2}\left(\dfrac{x}{2}\right)^{-\frac{1}{2}} \cdot \dfrac{1}{2} = \dfrac{-\sqrt{2}}{4\sqrt{x}}\sin\sqrt{\dfrac{x}{2}}$

93 **a** $D_x \sin(3x^2) = \cos(3x^2) \cdot 6x$

     b $D_x \sin(3x)^2 = \cos(3x)^2 \cdot 2(3x) \cdot 3 = 18x \cdot \cos(3x)^2$

     c $D_x \sin^2 3x = D_x(\sin 3x)^2 = 2(\sin 3x)(\cos 3x)3 = 6\sin 3x \cos 3x$

94 Since $-\dfrac{\pi}{2} \le u \le \dfrac{\pi}{2}$, $\cos u \ge 0$ and $\cos u = \sqrt{\cos^2 u}$.

     $\cos u = \sqrt{\cos^2 u} = \sqrt{1 - (\sin u)^2} = \sqrt{1 - x^2}$

95 $D_x(\sin u\big|^{u=\text{arcsin } x}) = D_x x = 1$; $\cos u \cdot D_x \arcsin x\big|^{u=\text{arcsin } x} = 1$; (see Frame 94); $\sqrt{1 - x^2} \cdot D_x \arcsin x = 1$; $D_x \arcsin x = \dfrac{1}{\sqrt{1 - x^2}}$.

96 Since $0 \le u \le \pi$, $\sin u \ge 0$ and $\sin u = \sqrt{\sin^2 u}$.

     $\sin u = \sqrt{\sin^2 u} = \sqrt{1 - (\cos u)^2} = \sqrt{1 - x^2}$

97 $D_x(\cos u\big|^{u=\text{arccos } x}) = D_x x = 1$; $-\sin u \cdot D_x \arccos x\big|^{u=\text{arccos } x} = 1$; (see Frame 96); $\sqrt{1 - x^2} \cdot D_x \arccos x = 1$; $D_x \arccos x = -\dfrac{1}{\sqrt{1 - x^2}}$.

98 From trigonometry, $\sec^2 u = 1 + \tan^2 u = 1 + x^2$. That $1 + \tan^2 u = \sec^2 u$ follows from $\cos^2 u + \sin^2 u = 1$ by dividing both sides of the equation by $\cos^2 u$.

99 $D_x(\tan u\big|^{u=\text{arctan } x}) = D_x x = 1$; $\sec^2 u \cdot D_x \arctan x = 1$; (see Frame 98); $(1 + x^2)D_x \arctan x = 1$; $D_x \arctan x = \dfrac{1}{1 + x^2}$.

We have now derived three additional derivative formulas which the student should proceed to memorize:

$$D_x \arcsin x = \frac{1}{\sqrt{1 - x^2}} \qquad D_x \arccos x = \frac{-1}{\sqrt{1 - x^2}}$$

$$D_x \arctan x = \frac{1}{1 + x^2}$$

100 $D_x \left(\arcsin u \big|^{u=g(x)} \right) = ?$

101 $D_x \left(\arccos u \big|^{u=g(x)} \right) = ?$

102 $D_x \left(\arctan u \big|^{u=g(x)} \right) = ?$

103 $D_x \arcsin \dfrac{x}{a} = ?$ Assume a is a constant.

104 $D_x \arccos \dfrac{x}{a} = ?$

105 $D_x \arctan \dfrac{x}{a} = ?$

106 $D_x \sqrt{\arccos x} = ?$

107 $D_x(\sqrt{x} \arccos \sqrt{x}) = ?$

108 $D_x \arcsin \sqrt{x} = ?$

109 $D_x \arctan \dfrac{1 + x}{1 - x} = ?$

110 $D_x(\arcsin x + x \sqrt{1 - x^2}) = ?$

111 $D_x \left(\arcsin x + \dfrac{\sqrt{1 - x^2}}{x} \right) = ?$

100 $\quad D_x \left(\arctan u |^{u=g(x)} \right) = \dfrac{1}{\sqrt{1-u^2}} g'(x) |^{u=g(x)} = \dfrac{g'(x)}{\sqrt{1-[g(x)]^2}}$

101 $\quad D_x \left(\arccos u |^{u=g(x)} \right) = \dfrac{-1}{\sqrt{1-u^2}} g'(x) |^{u=g(x)} = \dfrac{-g'(x)}{\sqrt{1-[g(x)]^2}}$

102 $\quad D_x \left(\arctan u |^{u=g(x)} \right) = \dfrac{1}{1+u^2} g'(x) |^{u=g(x)} = \dfrac{g'(x)}{1+[g(x)]^2}$

103 $\quad D_x \arcsin \dfrac{x}{a} = \dfrac{1}{\sqrt{1-(x/a)^2}} \dfrac{1}{a} = \dfrac{1}{\sqrt{a^2-x^2}}.$ Note that it is simpler

to deal with the product $\dfrac{1}{a} x$ than with the quotient $\dfrac{x}{a}.$

104 $\quad \dfrac{-1}{\sqrt{a^2-x^2}}$

105 $\quad D_x \arctan \dfrac{x}{a} = \dfrac{1}{1+(x/a)^2} \dfrac{1}{a} = \dfrac{a}{a^2+x^2}$

106 $\quad D_x(\arccos x)^{\frac{1}{2}} = \dfrac{1}{2} (\arccos x)^{-\frac{1}{2}} \dfrac{-1}{\sqrt{1-x^2}}$

107 $\quad D_x(\sqrt{x} \arccos \sqrt{x}) = \sqrt{x} \dfrac{-1}{\sqrt{1-(\sqrt{x})^2}} \dfrac{1}{2} x^{-\frac{1}{2}} + (\arccos \sqrt{x}) \dfrac{1}{2} x^{-\frac{1}{2}}$

$\qquad\qquad = \dfrac{-1}{2\sqrt{1-x}} + \dfrac{\arccos \sqrt{x}}{2\sqrt{x}}$

108 $\quad D_x \arcsin \sqrt{x} = \dfrac{1}{\sqrt{1-(\sqrt{x})^2}} \dfrac{1}{2} x^{-\frac{1}{2}} = \dfrac{1}{2\sqrt{x}\sqrt{1-x}}$

109 $\quad D_x \arctan \dfrac{1+x}{1-x} = \dfrac{1}{1+\left(\dfrac{1+x}{1-x}\right)^2} \dfrac{(1-x)-(1+x)(-1)}{(1-x)^2} = \dfrac{1}{1+x^2}$

110 $\quad \dfrac{1}{\sqrt{1-x^2}} + \left[x \dfrac{1}{2} (1-x^2)^{-\frac{1}{2}}(-2x) + \sqrt{1-x^2} \right] = 2\sqrt{1-x^2}$

111 $\quad \dfrac{1}{\sqrt{1-x^2}} + \dfrac{x^{\frac{1}{2}}(1-x^2)^{-\frac{1}{2}}(-2x) - \sqrt{1-x^2}}{x^2} = \dfrac{-\sqrt{1-x^2}}{x^2}$

112 $D_x \arctan \sqrt{x} = ?$

113 From the theory of logarithms, $\ln e^x = x \ln e = x \cdot 1 = x$. Start with $D_x \ln e^x = D_x x$ and derive the formula for the derivative of e^x from that of the logarithmic function.

114 Since $\ln a^x = x \ln a$ (where a is a positive constant), start with $D_x \ln a^x = D_x(x \ln a)$ and derive a formula for the derivative of a^x.

115 Let $f(x) = (\sin x)^x$. Then, $\ln f(x) = \ln (\sin x)^x = x \cdot \ln (\sin x)$. Start with $D_x \ln f(x) = D_x(x \cdot \ln \sin x)$ and find $D_x f(x)$.

116 Let $f(x) = x^a$. Then, $\ln f(x) = a \ln x$. Start with $D_x \ln f(x) = D_x(a \ln x)$ and derive the formula $D_x x^a = ax^{a-1}$. We are tacitly assuming $x > 0$.

Second- and Higher-order Derivatives If $f(x)$ is a function, then we denote the *second* derivative of f by $D_x^2 f$. It is the derivative of the (first) derivative of f: $D_x^2 f = D_x(D_x f)$. For example, if $f(x) = x^3 + 3x^2 + 2x + 5$, then $D_x f = 3x^2 + 6x + 2$, and $D_x^2 f = 6x + 6$. Again, if $f(x)$ is a function, alternate notation for the derivative of f was $f'(x)$. Similar notation for the second derivative is $f''(x)$.

Third and higher derivatives may also be defined, and the notation used is $D_x^3 f, f'''(x), f^{(3)}(x), D_x^4 f, f^{(4)}(x)$, etc. They are defined naturally: the third derivative is the derivative of the second derivative function, $D_x^3 f = D_x(D_x^2 f)$, $D_x^4 f = D_x(D_x^3 f)$, etc. For the example above, $D_x^2 f = 6x + 6$, $D_x^3 f = 6$, $D_x^4 f = 0$, $D_x^5 f = 0$, etc.

If y is a function of x, the Leibnitz notation for its derivative is $\dfrac{dy}{dx}$. Corresponding notation for second and higher derivatives is $\dfrac{d^2y}{dx^2}, \dfrac{d^3y}{dx^3}$, etc.

---

117 If $f(x) = x^3 - 7x^2 + 5x - 1$, find $D_x f, D_x^2 f, D_x^3 f, D_x^4 f, D_x^5 f$.

118 Find $D_t^2(t \sqrt{t} - 2t)$.

119 If $f(x) = \sqrt{3 + x}$, find $f'''(x)$.

112 $\dfrac{1}{1+x}\dfrac{1}{2}x^{-\frac{1}{2}} = \dfrac{1}{2(1+x)\sqrt{x}}$

113 $\ln e^x = x;\ D_x \ln e^x = 1;\ \dfrac{1}{e^x} D_x e^x = 1;\ D_x e^x = e^x.$

114 $D_x \ln a^x = D_x(\ln a)x = \ln a;\ \dfrac{1}{a^x} D_x a^x = \ln a;\ D_x a^x = a^x \cdot \ln a.$

115 $D_x \ln f(x) = D_x(x \cdot \ln \sin x);\ \dfrac{1}{f(x)} D_x f = x\,\dfrac{1}{\sin x} \cos x + \ln \sin x;$

$D_x f = f(x)\left(\dfrac{x \cdot \cos x}{\sin x} + \ln \sin x\right) = (\sin x)^x \left(\dfrac{x \cdot \cos x}{\sin x} + \ln \sin x\right).$

This method is applicable whenever dealing with exponents, when the exponent itself is a function. The exponential form is reduced to a product by first taking the logarithm of the function.

116 $D_x \ln f(x) = D_x(a \ln x);\ \dfrac{1}{f(x)} D_x f = a\,\dfrac{1}{x};$

$D_x f = f(x)a\,\dfrac{1}{x} = x^a a\,\dfrac{1}{x} = ax^{a-1}.$

117 $D_x f = 3x^2 - 14x + 5 \qquad D_x^2 f = 6x - 14 \qquad D_x^3 f = 6$

$D_x^4 f = 0 \qquad D_x^5 f = 0$

118 $D_t(t^{\frac{3}{2}} - 2t) = \frac{3}{2}t^{\frac{1}{2}} - 2 \qquad D_t^2(t^{\frac{3}{2}} - 2t) = \frac{3}{4}t^{-\frac{1}{2}}$

119 $f'(x) = \frac{1}{2}(3 + x)^{-\frac{1}{2}} \qquad f''(x) = -\frac{1}{4}(3 + x)^{-\frac{3}{2}} \qquad f'''(x) = \frac{3}{8}(3 + x)^{-\frac{5}{2}}$

120 If $y = (3x + 2)^{\frac{1}{3}}$, find $\dfrac{d^3y}{dx^3}$.

121 Find $D_x^2(xe^x)$.

122 If $f(x) = x^2 e^x$, find $f''(x)$.

123 If $y = \ln{(x^2 + 1)}$, find $\dfrac{d^2y}{dx^2}$.

124 Find $D_x^2(x^2 \ln x)$.

125 Find $D_x^2 \frac{1}{2}(e^x + e^{-x})$.

126 Find $D_x^2 e^{ax} \sin bx$.

127 $D_x^2 \tan x = ?$

128 $D_x^2 \csc^2 x = ?$

129 If $f(x) = \arcsin x$, find $f''(x)$.

130 If $y = \arctan x$, find $\dfrac{d^2y}{dx^2}$.

Partial Derivatives If $f(x,y)$ is a function of the two variables x and y defined in some region of the xy plane, then the *partial derivative* of f with respect to x is, operationally, the derivative of f with respect to x where y *is considered to be a constant.* Similarly the partial derivative of f with respect to y is the derivative of f considered as a function of y alone, with x constant. Notations for the partial derivative with respect to x are

$$D_x f(x,y) \qquad \frac{\partial f}{\partial x} \qquad \frac{\partial}{\partial x} f \qquad f_x(x,y) \qquad f_1(x,y)$$

and for the partial derivative with respect to y are

$$D_y f(x,y) \qquad \frac{\partial f}{\partial y} \qquad \frac{\partial}{\partial y} f \qquad f_y(x,y) \qquad f_2(x,y)$$

Consider, for example, $f(x,y) = y \cdot x^2$. Then $f_x(x,y) = y \cdot 2x$. You should have no difficulty finding the derivative $D_x(ax^2) = 2ax$, since you are

120 This is the Leibnitz notation for the third derivative of a function.

$$\frac{dy}{dx} = (3x + 2)^{-\frac{2}{3}} \qquad \frac{d^2y}{dx^2} = -2(3x + 2)^{-\frac{5}{3}} \qquad \frac{d^3y}{dx^3} = 10(3x + 2)^{-\frac{8}{3}}$$

121 $D_x(xe^x) = xe^x + e^x = (x + 1)e^x$
$D_x^2(xe^x) = (x + 1)e^x + e^x = (x + 2)e^x$

122 $f'(x) = x^2e^x + e^x2x = (x^2 + 2x)e^x$
$f''(x) = (x^2 + 2x)e^x + e^x(2x + 2) = (x^2 + 4x + 2)e^x$

123 $\dfrac{dy}{dx} = \dfrac{2x}{1 + x^2} \qquad \dfrac{d^2y}{dx^2} = \dfrac{2(1 - x^2)}{(1 + x^2)^2}$

124 $D_x(x^2 \ln x) = x + 2x \ln x \qquad D_x^2(x^2 \ln x) = 3 + 2 \ln x$

125 $D_x^2\frac{1}{2}(e^x + e^{-x}) = \frac{1}{2}(e^x + e^{-x})$

126 $e^{ax}[(a^2 - b^2) \sin (bx) + 2ab \cos (bx)]$

127 $2 \sec^2 x \tan x$

128 $2(\csc^2 x)(\csc^2 x + 2 \cot^2 x)$

129 $x(1 - x^2)^{-\frac{3}{2}}$

130 $\dfrac{d^2y}{dx^2} = \dfrac{-2x}{(1 + x^2)^2}$

accustomed to consider the symbol a as a constant. Perhaps, for the first few problems, it may be instructive to replace the symbol y by a, find the derivative, then replace a by y. Further, for the same example, $f_y(x,y) = x^2$.

131 If $f(x,y) = x + y$, find $f_x(x,y)$ and $f_y(x,y)$.

132 If $f(x,y) = xy^2$, find $f_x(x,y)$ and $f_y(x,y)$.

133 If $f(x,y) = x \sin y$, find $f_1(x,y)$ and $f_2(x,y)$. Read $f_1(x,y)$ as the partial derivative of $f(x,y)$ with respect to its first variable, i.e., x; and read $f_2(x,y)$ as the partial derivative of $f(x,y)$ with respect to its second variable y.

134 If $f(x,y) = e^{x/y}$, find $\dfrac{\partial f}{\partial x}$ and $\dfrac{\partial f}{\partial y}$.

135 If $f(x,y) = y^2 \ln x$, find $f_x(x,y)$ and $f_y(x,y)$.

136 If $f(x,y) = \dfrac{x + y}{x - y}$, find $\dfrac{\partial}{\partial x} f(x,y)$ and $\dfrac{\partial}{\partial y} f(x,y)$.

Higher-order Partial Derivatives Given a function of two variables $f(x,y)$, there are four second (partial) derivatives:

1   first with respect to x, then with respect to x:

$$D_{xx}^2 f(x,y) \qquad \frac{\partial^2 f}{\partial x^2} \qquad f_{xx}(x,y) \qquad f_{11}(x,y)$$

2   first with respect to x, then with respect to y:

$$D_y D_x f(x,y) \qquad \frac{\partial^2 f}{\partial y \partial x} \qquad f_{xy}(x,y) \qquad f_{12}(x,y)$$

3   first with respect to y, then with respect to x:

$$D_x D_y f(x,y) \qquad \frac{\partial^2 f}{\partial x \partial y} \qquad f_{yx}(x,y) \qquad f_{21}(x,y)$$

131 $f_x(x,y) = 1 + 0 = 1$ (y is a constant; its derivative is 0)
$f_y(x,y) = 0 + 1 = 1$

132 $f_x(x,y) = y^2$ $f_y(x,y) = x \cdot 2y = 2xy$

133 $f_1(x,y) = \sin y$ $f_2(x,y) = x \cos y$

134 $\dfrac{\partial f}{\partial x} = e^{x/y} \dfrac{1}{y}$ $\dfrac{\partial f}{\partial y} = e^{x/y}(-x/y^2)$

135 $f_x(x,y) = y^2 \dfrac{1}{x}$ $f_y(x,y) = (\ln x)2y$

136 $\dfrac{\partial}{\partial x} f(x,y) = \dfrac{-2y}{(x-y)^2}$ $\dfrac{\partial}{\partial y} f(x,y) = \dfrac{2x}{(x-y)^2}$

4   first with respect to y, then with respect to y:

$$D_{yy}{}^2 f(x,y) \qquad \frac{\partial^2 f}{\partial y^2} \qquad f_{yy}(x,y) \qquad f_{22}(x,y)$$

The apparent inconsistency in the symbol order in 2 and 3 is explainable as follows: $\dfrac{\partial^2 f}{\partial y \partial x} = \dfrac{\partial}{\partial y}\left(\dfrac{\partial f}{\partial x}\right)$, while $f_{xy}(x,y) = (f_x)_y(x,y)$ or $f_{12}(x,y) = (f_1)_2(x,y)$. For a function of two variables there are thus eight third-partial derivatives.

For example, to find $\dfrac{\partial^2 f}{\partial x \partial y}$ when $f(x,y) = x^2 \cdot \sin y$: first, with x constant,

$\dfrac{\partial f}{\partial y} = x^2 \cdot \cos y$; then, with y constant in $\dfrac{\partial f}{\partial y}$, $\dfrac{\partial^2 f}{\partial x \partial y} = \dfrac{\partial}{\partial x}\left(\dfrac{\partial f}{\partial y}\right) = 2x \cdot \cos y$.

The same function results for $\dfrac{\partial^2 f}{\partial y \partial x}$, and this property obtains for all sufficiently nice functions.

---

137   If $f(x,y) = y^2 \ln x$, find $\dfrac{\partial^2 f}{\partial x^2}, \dfrac{\partial^2 f}{\partial y \partial x}, \dfrac{\partial^2 f}{\partial y^2}, \dfrac{\partial^2 f}{\partial x \partial y}$.

138   If $f(x,y) = x^2 y + xy^2$, find $f_{xx}, f_{xy}, f_{yx}, f_{yy}$.

139   For each of the following specify the *order* of taking derivatives. (a) $\dfrac{\partial^2 f}{\partial x \partial y}$; (b) $f_{xy}(x,y)$; (c) $f_{11}(x,y)$; (d) $f_{21}(x,y)$; (e) $\dfrac{\partial^2 f}{\partial y \partial x}$.

140   If $f(x,y) = x^2 + xy + y^2$, evaluate $\dfrac{\partial^2 f}{\partial x^2} + \dfrac{\partial^2 f}{\partial y^2}$.

141   If $f(x,y) = e^x \sin y$, evaluate $\dfrac{\partial^2 f}{\partial x^2} + \dfrac{\partial^2 f}{\partial y^2}$.

142   Show that $f(x,y) = \ln(x^2 + y^2)$ is a harmonic function.

137 $\dfrac{\partial f}{\partial x} = \dfrac{y^2}{x}$ $\dfrac{\partial f}{\partial y} = 2y \ln x$ $\dfrac{\partial^2 f}{\partial x^2} = \dfrac{-y^2}{x^2}$ $\dfrac{\partial^2 f}{\partial y \partial x} = \dfrac{2y}{x}$

$\dfrac{\partial^2 f}{\partial y^2} = 2 \ln x$ $\dfrac{\partial^2 f}{\partial x \partial y} = \dfrac{2y}{x}$

138 $f_x(x,y) = 2xy + y^2$ $f_y(x,y) = x^2 + 2xy$ $f_{xx}(x,y) = 2y$
$f_{xy}(x,y) = 2x + 2y$ $f_{yy}(x,y) = 2x$ $f_{yx}(x,y) = 2x + 2y$

139 (a) first with respect to y, then with respect to x: y,x; (b) x,y; (c) x,x; (d) y,x; (e)x,y.

140 $\dfrac{\partial f}{\partial x} = 2x + y$ $\dfrac{\partial f}{\partial y} = x + 2y$ $\dfrac{\partial^2 f}{\partial y^2} = 2$ $\dfrac{\partial^2 f}{\partial x^2} = 2$

$\dfrac{\partial^2 f}{\partial x^2} + \dfrac{\partial^2 f}{\partial y^2} = 2 + 2 = 4$

141 $\dfrac{\partial^2 f}{\partial x^2} + \dfrac{\partial^2 f}{\partial y^2} = 0$.   A function satisfying this partial-differential equation is called a *harmonic* function.

142 $\dfrac{\partial^2 f}{\partial x^2} + \dfrac{\partial^2 f}{\partial y^2} = \dfrac{2(y^2 - x^2)}{(x^2 + y^2)^2} + \dfrac{2(x^2 - y^2)}{(x^2 + y^2)^2} = 0$

The partial-derivative concept extends in a natural way to functions of more than two variables. If $F(x,y,z)$ is a function of three variables, then $\frac{\partial F}{\partial y}$, for example, is its derivative when it is considered as a function of y alone, with both x and z as constants. Thus if $F(x,y,z) = x + \sin(yz)$, then $\frac{\partial F}{\partial y} = z \cos(yz)$. Higher-order partial derivatives are similarly defined.

143 If $F(x,y,z) = xy^2z^3$, find all first-partial derivatives and all nine second-partial derivatives.

144 If $F(x,y,z) = x^2e^y \sin z$, find all first-partial derivatives and all nine second-partial derivatives.

143 $\quad F_x = y^2z^3 \qquad F_{xx} = 0 \qquad F_{xy} = 2yz^3 \qquad F_{xz} = 3y^2z^2$
$\quad\quad\;\; F_y = 2xyz^3 \qquad F_{yx} = 2yz^3 \qquad F_{yy} = 2xz^3 \qquad F_{yz} = 6xyz^2$
$\quad\quad\;\; F_z = 3xy^2z^2 \qquad F_{zx} = 3y^2z^2 \qquad F_{zy} = 6xyz^2 \qquad F_{zz} = 6xy^2z$

144 $\quad F_x = 2xe^y \sin z \qquad F_{xx} = 2e^y \sin z \qquad F_{xy} = 2xe^y \sin z$
$$F_{xz} = 2xe^y \cos z$$

$\quad\quad\;\; F_y = x^2e^y \sin z \qquad F_{yx} = 2xe^y \sin z \qquad F_{yy} = x^2e^y \sin z$
$$F_{yz} = x^2e^y \cos z$$

$\quad\quad\;\; F_z = x^2e^y \cos z \qquad F_{zx} = 2xe^y \cos z \qquad F_{zy} = x^2e^y \cos z$
$$F_{zz} = -x^2e^y \sin z$$

chapter 3

The Area Curves of a Function;
The Antiderivative

In Chap. 1 we constructed the *slope curve* of a given function. Here we will construct an *area curve* of a given function. While the slope curve for a function was unique, each function has many area curves, depending on the selection of the vertical line from which the area will be measured. On each of the graphs in Figs. I to VII, we have selected a point P_0 and will measure the area from the vertical line through P_0. We illustrate first with the graph of the cosine curve of Fig. V. Draw vertical lines through P_0 and P_2. By counting squares and estimating portions thereof, we determine the area bounded by the curve, the x axis, and the vertical lines through P_0 and P_2. We are interested in "signed" areas, the sign to be determined by the following convention. If P_2 is to the right of P_0, then regions *above* the x axis will be considered to have *positive* areas and regions *below* the x axis, *negative* areas. If P_2 is to the left of P_0, the conventions are reversed: regions above the x axis will be considered to have negative areas and those below the x axis, positive areas. When a region lies partially above and

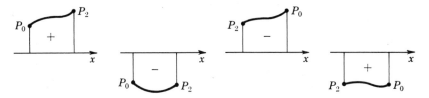

partially below the x axis, its signed area is the *algebraic sum* of the portions above and below the x axis.

1 a Frame 1 refers to the graph of the cosine curve of Fig. V. Draw vertical lines through P_0 and P_2, and, by counting squares, find the signed area of the region bounded by these two vertical lines, the graph of the curve, and the x axis.

1 a Each square represents 0.0025 square unit. There are approximately 285 squares in the region, hence, 0.71 square unit. Since P_2 is to the right of P_0 and the region is above the x axis, the signed area is positive.

b Write an ordered pair of numbers, the first coordinate being the abscissa of the point P_2, and the second being the signed area of the region described in Frame **1a**.

c Draw a vertical line through P_3 and find the signed area of the region bounded by the vertical lines through P_0 and P_3, the curve, and the x axis. Write an ordered pair of numbers, the first coordinate of which is the abscissa of the point P_3 and the second coordinate, the signed area of the region described.

d Follow the instructions of Frame **1c** for the point P_{10}.

e Follow the instructions of Frame **1c** for the point P_4.

f Follow the instructions of Frame **1c** for the points P_5, P_6, . . . , P_9.

g Including the ordered pair of numbers $(0,0)$, the first coordinate of which is the *abscissa of the point* P_0 and the second coordinate the zero area measured from P_0 to P_0, plot on a second coordinate system prepared to the same scale as Fig. V all the ordered pairs determined in Frame **1b** to **f**, then draw a smooth curve connecting these points. Compare this curve with those of Figs. I to VII.

2 a In this frame, we are going to determine the area curve of the $2x$ function measured from P_0 of Fig. I. Instead of counting squares, it will be easier here to *compute* the signed areas of the regions. Draw vertical lines through P_0 and P_1 and compute the area of the triangle bounded by these vertical lines, the graph of the $2x$ function, and the x axis. Write an ordered pair of numbers with first coordinate the abscissa of P_1 and second coordinate the signed area of the triangular region.

b Follow the instructions of Frame **2a** for P_2, P_3.

c Follow the instructions of Frame **2a** for P_4, P_5.

b (0.8, 0.71)

c (1.6, 1.0). Since P_3 is to the right of P_0 and the region lies above the x axis, the signed area of the region is positive.

d (−0.8, −0.72). Since P_{10} is to the left of P_0 and the region is above the x axis, the signed area is negative.

e (2.8, 0.33). Here a portion of the area lies above and a portion lies below the x axis. From P_0 to P_3 the area is positive, about 1.0 square unit; from P_3 to P_4 it is negative, about 0.67 square unit. The algebraic sum is +0.33.

f At P_5: (3.1, 0); at P_6: (4.0, −0.76); at P_7: (4.7, −1); at P_8: (5.5, −0.70); at P_9: (6.3, 0).

g The curve is the graph of the sine function. As constructed this curve is called the *area curve* of the cosine function as measured from P_0. Thus *the area curve of the cosine function* (measured from P_0) *is the graph of the sine function.*

2 a (0.5, 0.25)

b At P_2: (1,1); at P_3: (2,4).

c At P_4: (−0.5, 0.25); at P_5: (−1,1). Here the points are to the left of P_0 and the regions are below the x axis; thus the signed areas of the regions are positive.

d Along with (0,0) = (abscissa of P_0, area from P_0 to P_0), plot all ordered pairs determined in Frame **2a** to **c** on a second coordinate system prepared to the same scale as Fig. I, draw a smooth curve through these points, and compare this area curve with those of Figs. I to VII.

3 Find a function whose derivative is $\cos x$.

4 Find an antiderivative of $2x$, i.e., a function whose derivative is $2x$.

5 a Consider the graph of the function e^x of Fig. VII. Draw vertical lines through P_0 and P_1 and find (by counting squares) the area of the region bounded by these vertical lines, the curve, and the x axis. Write an ordered pair of numbers having first coordinate the abscissa of P_1 and second coordinate the signed area of the designated region.

b Follow the instructions of Frame **5a** for P_4, P_5, P_6, P_7.

c Follow the instructions of Frame **5a** for P_2, P_3.

d Along with (0,0) = (abscissa of P_0, area from P_0 to P_0), plot the ordered pairs determined in Frame **5a** to **c** on a second coordinate system prepared to the same scale as Fig. VII, draw a smooth curve through these points, and compare this area curve with those of Figs. I to VII.

6 a Consider the graph of the reciprocal function $1/x$ of Fig. VII. Draw vertical lines through P_0 and P_1 and find the area of the region bounded by these vertical lines, the curve, and the x axis. Write an ordered pair of real numbers, the first coordinate of which is the abscissa of P_1, and the second coordinate of which is the signed area of the region.

b Follow the instructions of Frame **6a** for points P_2, P_3, P_4.

c Along with (1,0) = (abscissa of P_0, area from P_0 to P_0), plot the ordered pairs in Frame **6a** and **b** on a second coordinate system prepared to the same scale as Fig. VII, draw a smooth curve through these points, and compare this curve with those of Figs. I to VII.

d The area curve of the $2x$ function (measured from P_0) is precisely the graph of the x^2 function. In Frame 1 we found that the area curve of the *cosine* function is the graph of the *sine* function. In both cases note that the derivative of the area function is the original function, and we may suspect that the area curve of a given function is the graph of a second function whose derivative equals the given function.

3 One such function is $\sin x$, but the answer is *not unique*. The derivative of $1 + \sin x$ is also $\cos x$, as is $k + \sin x$ for any constant k. Had we, in Frame 1, measured areas from some point other than P_0, the area curve would have been one of these: had we started from P_2 our area curve would have been the graph of $-0.72 + \sin x$; had we started from P_3 the area curve would have been the graph of $-1 + \sin x$. Any such function, i.e., any function whose derivative is $\cos x$, is called *an antiderivative* of $\cos x$.

4 x^2 or $x^2 + 1$ or $x^2 + k$, for any constant k. Relate these to the area curve of the $2x$ function; see Frame 2.

5 a $(-1, -0.64)$. Since P_1 is to the left of P_0 and the region lies *above* the x axis, the signed area is negative.

b At P_4: $(0.5, 0.65)$; at P_5: $(1,1.7)$; at P_6: $(1.3, 2.7)$; at P_7: $(2,6.4)$.

c At P_2: $(-0.5, -0.39)$; at P_3: $(0,0)$, since P_3 coincides with P_0.

d The area curve resembles the graph of e^x; it is actually the graph of e^x translated 1 unit downward, thus the graph of $e^x - 1$. Note that $e^x - 1$ is an antiderivative of e^x, since $D_x(e^x - 1) = e^x$.

6 a $(0.25, -1.4)$. Since P_1 is to the left of P_0 and the region is above the x axis, the signed area is negative.

b At P_2: $(0.5, -0.7)$; at P_3: $(2,0.7)$; at P_4: $(4,1.4)$.

c The area curve of the reciprocal function (measured from P_0) is the graph of the logarithm function $\ln x$. Again note the antiderivative relationship $D_x \ln x = 1/x$, and note that the area function of the reciprocal function as measured from P_0 is an antiderivative of the reciprocal function. For the points which lie to the left of the y axis, no clearly defined region exists, hence no area function is thus defined for negative values of x.

7 Find an antiderivative of $\sin x$, that is, a function whose derivative is $\sin x$.

8 Find an antiderivative of $3x^2$.

9 Find an antiderivative of x^2.

10 Find an antiderivative of (a) $4x^3$; (b) x^3.

11 Find an antiderivative of (a) $5x^4$; (b) x^4.

12 Find an antiderivative of (a) $(n+1)x^n$; (b) x^n. Assume $n \neq -1$.

13 Find antiderivatives of x^5, x^6, $x^{\frac{1}{2}}$, $x^{-\frac{1}{2}}$, $x^{-\frac{3}{2}}$.

14 Find an antiderivative of x^{-1}.

15 Find an antiderivative of (a) $\sec^2 x$; (b) $\csc^2 x$. Review the derivative formulas memorized while working in Chap. 2. Do you remember a function whose derivative is $\sec^2 x$? $\csc^2 x$?

16 Find an antiderivative of (a) $\sec x \cdot \tan x$; (b) $\csc x \cdot \cot x$.

17 Find an antiderivative of e^x.

18 Find an antiderivative of $1/\sqrt{1 - x^2}$. Review again the derivative formulas memorized in Chap. 2. These are listed following Frame 28.

The Indefinite Integral   For the phrase "an antiderivative of $f(x)$" we write the symbol $\int f(x)\, dx$. Both the "$\int$," called the *integral sign*, and the "dx" are part of the symbol, the latter serving no useful purpose at the moment.   It will however be utilized as we extend our procedures for finding antiderivatives beyond those of pure recognition.   An alternative reading of the symbol $\int f(x)\, dx$ is "the *indefinite* integral of $f(x)$."

---

19 $\int e^x dx = ?$

7 $-\cos x$ or $-\cos x + C$, where C is any constant. We will generally write our answer in the latter form: $-\cos x + C$. There is no *method* here; at this stage our ability to find an antiderivative depends entirely on our recollection of the derivative formulas. Here, $D_x \cos x = -\sin x$, hence $D_x(-\cos x) = \sin x$.

8 $x^3 + C$ $D_x(x^3 + C) = 3x^2$

9 $\frac{1}{3}x^3 + C$ $D_x(\frac{1}{3}x^3 + C) = \frac{1}{3}3x^2 = x^2$

10 (a) $x^4 + C$; (b) $\frac{1}{4}x^4 + C$ $D_x(\frac{1}{4}x^4 + C) = \frac{1}{4}4x^3 = x^3$

11 (a) $x^5 + C$; (b) $\frac{1}{5}x^5 + C$

12 (a) $x^{n+1} + C$; (b) $\dfrac{1}{n+1} x^{n+1} + C$

$D_x(x^{n+1} + C) = (n+1)x^n$

$D_x\left(\dfrac{1}{n+1} x^{n+1} + C\right) = \dfrac{1}{n+1}(n+1)x^n = x^n$

13 $\frac{1}{6}x^6 + C$ $\frac{1}{7}x^7 + C$ $\frac{2}{3}x^{\frac{3}{2}} + C$ $2x^{\frac{1}{2}} + C$ $3x^{\frac{1}{3}} + C$
Check each of these by taking derivatives.

14 An application of the formula of Frame **12** will not work here; the symbol $\frac{1}{0} x^0$ is meaningless. Note that $x^{-1} = 1/x$, and an antiderivative of $1/x$ is $\ln x + C$.

15 (a) $\tan x + C$; (b) $-\cot x + C$
$D_x(\tan x + C) = \sec^2 x$ $D_x(-\cot x + C) = \csc^2 x$

16 (a) $\sec x + C$; (b) $-\csc x + C$
$D_x(-\csc x + C) = \csc x \cot x$

17 $e^x + C$ $D_x(e^x + C) = e^x$

18 $\arcsin x + C$ or $-\arccos x + C$

19 $\int e^x\, dx = e^x + C$. This is merely a restatement of Frame **17**; the symbol $\int e^x\, dx$ is merely the symbol for an antiderivative of e^x.

20 $\int \dfrac{1}{\sqrt{1 - x^2}}\, dx = ?$

21 $\int 2\, dx = ?$

22 $\int dx = ?$

23 $\int (x^2 + 5)\, dx = ?$ You will have to do some guessing here; guess, then check.

24 $\int 5 \cos x\, dx = ?$ Again, guess an answer, then check it.

25 $\int \dfrac{1}{1 + x^2}\, dx = ?$ Are you starting to appreciate the need for memorizing the derivative formulas exhibited in Chap. 2?   A list of these formulas follows Frame **28** in Chap. 2.   Success with the technique of integration demands mastery of these formulas and recognition of the functions which appear as derivatives.

26 $\int \sqrt{x}\, dx = ?$

27 $\int x^{-1}\, dx = ?$

28 Is $\int \tan x\, dx = \sec^2 x + C$?

20 $\int \dfrac{1}{\sqrt{1-x^2}}\, dx = \arcsin x + C$ or $-\arccos x + C$. This is merely a restatement of Frame **18**.

21 We seek an antiderivative of 2. Since $D_x(2x + C) = 2$, $\int 2dx = 2x + C$. If you obtained 0 as your answer, you confused the *derivative* with the *antiderivative*.

22 This is an apparently meaningless symbol. We interpret it as $\int 1\, dx = ?$ Then, since $D_x x = 1$, $\int 1\, dx = x + C$.

23 $\frac{1}{3}x^3 + 5x + C$. Since the derivative of the sum of two functions is the sum of their derivatives, the same can be said for the indefinite integral (antiderivative) of the sum of two functions:
$$\int (x^2 + 5)\, dx = \int x^2\, dx + \int 5\, dx = \tfrac{1}{3}x^3 + 5x + C.$$

24 $5 \sin x + C$. This is easily seen by inspection. However since $D(kf) = kDf$, we also have $\int kf(x)\, dx = k\int f(x)\, dx$; i.e., *the integral of the product of a constant by a function equals the product of the constant by the integral of the function.*

25 $\arctan x + C$

26 $\frac{2}{3}x^{\frac{3}{2}} + C \qquad D_x(\frac{2}{3}x^{\frac{3}{2}} + C) = \frac{2}{3} \cdot \frac{3}{2}x^{\frac{1}{2}} = x^{\frac{1}{2}} = \sqrt{x}$

27 Not $\frac{1}{0}x^0$, this is meaningless; not $(-1)x^{-2}$, this is the derivative of x^{-1}; but $\ln x + C$. $D_x(\ln x + C) = 1/x = x^{-1}$.

28 No. To evaluate $\int \tan x\, dx$ we seek a function whose derivative is $\tan x$ and $D_x(\sec^2 x) = 2\sec^2 x \tan x \neq \tan x$. An antiderivative of $\tan x$ is $-\ln \cos x$, since $D_x(-\ln \cos x) = -\dfrac{1}{\cos x}(-\sin x) = \tan x$, but at this stage you could not be expected to obtain this result.

The statement $\int f(x)\,dx = F(x) + C$ means that $F(x)$ is an antiderivative of $f(x)$, i.e., $D_x F = f$, and that any antiderivative of $f(x)$ can be written as $F(x)$ added to some constant. The question $\int f(x)\,dx = ?$ requests the discovery of the antiderivative $F(x) + C$ of $f(x)$. At the moment the only means at the student's disposal for such discovery lies in recognition via his memorization of the derivative formulas. The exercises of this chapter are designed to extend the student's ability to discover antiderivatives. The operation of finding an antiderivative is called *indefinite integration*, the symbol $\int f(x)\,dx$ is called the *indefinite integral* of f, and the function $f(x)$ is called the *integrand* of the (indefinite) integral.

A short table of integrals appears on pages 161–165. References to formulas in this table will be frequently made. For example, the reference $\int 17$ is to the tabulated formula numbered 17. The student should mark those formulas which are derived as they are derived; these may then be applied to later problems. One of the goals of this program is to develop the student's facility in the use of tables of integrals as well as his mastery of the standard techniques of integration.

1 $\int \cos x \, dx = ?$

2 $\int \sin x \, dx = ?$

3 $\int \sec^2 x \, dx = ?$

4 Why is the following statement false: $\int \tan x \, dx = \sec^2 x + C$?

5 $\int 3x^2 \, dx = ?$

6 $\int x^2 \, dx = ?$

1 $\int \cos x\, dx = \sin x + C$, because $D_x \sin x = \cos x$. (See $\int 46$.) (Note: In your integral tables, check off the integration formulas referred to. Once a tabulated formula has been derived, it may be applied to other problems.)

2 $\int \sin x\, dx = -\cos x + C$. If you omitted the $(-)$ sign, you found the derivative of $\sin x$, not a function whose derivative is $\sin x$. To obtain the correct result it is necessary to think one step beyond the derivative formula $D_x \cos x = -\sin x$ to obtain $D_x(-\cos x) = \sin x$. (See $\int 45$.)

3 $\int \sec^2 x\, dx = \tan x + C$, because $D_x \tan x = \sec^2 x$. (See $\int 71$.)

4 $D_x \sec^2 x = 2 \sec x \sec x \tan x \neq \tan x$. Hence $\int \tan x\, dx \neq \sec^2 x + C$.

5 $\int 3x^2\, dx = x^3 + C$, since $D_x x^3 = 3x^2$.

6 $\int x^2\, dx = \frac{1}{3}x^3 + C$. This, again, is one step beyond the derivative formula $D_x x^3 = 3x^2$. From this it is not difficult to obtain $D_x(\frac{1}{3}x^3) = \frac{1}{3} \cdot 3x^2 = x^2$. The important idea here lies in noting that the derivative of a power function x^a reduces the exponent by 1: $D_x x^a = ax^{a-1}$. Hence the indefinite integral of a power function will *increase* the power by 1. The appropriate constant can be assigned by trial.

7 $\int x^4 \, dx = ?$

8 $\int x^5 \, dx = ?$

9 From the results of the last three frames, can you guess $\int x^a = ?$

10 $\int \sqrt{x} \, dx = ?$

11 $\int x^{-\frac{2}{3}} \, dx = ?$

12 $\int dx = ?$

13 $\int e^x \, dx = ?$

14 $\int x^e \, dx = ?$

15 $\int x^{-\frac{1}{3}} \, dx = ?$

16 $\int x^{-1} \, dx = ?$

17 Does the formula $\int x^a \, dx = \dfrac{1}{a+1} x^{a+1} + C$ obtain for all numbers a?

18 $\displaystyle\int \frac{1}{\sqrt{1 - x^2}} \, dx = ?$

19 $\int \sec x \tan x \, dx = ?$

7 $\int x^4\,dx = \frac{1}{5}x^5 + C$, since $D_x(\frac{1}{5}x^5) = \frac{1}{5}5x^4 = x^4$.

8 $\int x^5\,dx = \frac{1}{6}x^6 + C$

9 $\displaystyle\int x^a\,dx = \frac{1}{a+1}\,x^{a+1} + C$. Is this true for all numbers a? Try in turn $a = 2$, $a = 1$, $a = 0$, $a = -1$, $a = -2$.

10 $\int \sqrt{x}\,dx = \int x^{\frac{1}{2}}\,dx = \frac{2}{3}x^{\frac{3}{2}} + C$

11 $\int x^{-\frac{2}{3}}\,dx = 3x^{\frac{1}{3}} + C$

12 Think of this as $\int 1\,dx$. Thus $\int dx = \int 1\,dx = x + C$, since $D_x x = 1$.

13 $\int e^x\,dx = e^x + C$. If you obtained the incorrect result $\dfrac{1}{x+1}\,e^{x+1}$, you confused the exponential function e^x with the power function. Distinguish, again, e^x from x^e. (See $\int 93$.)

14 $\displaystyle\int x^e\,dx = \frac{1}{e+1}\,x^{e+1} + C$. The integrand here is a power function.

15 $\int x^{-\frac{1}{5}}\,dx = \frac{5}{4}x^{\frac{4}{5}} + C$

16 We hope you did not write the meaningless answer $\frac{1}{0}x^0$.
$$\int x^{-1}\,dx = \int \frac{1}{x}\,dx = \ln x + C, \text{ since } D_x \ln x = \frac{1}{x}. \quad \text{(See } \int 4.)$$

17 It is not true when $a = -1$; otherwise it is. $\int x^{-1}\,dx = \ln x + C$. (See $\int 3, 4$.)

18 $\displaystyle\int \frac{1}{\sqrt{1-x^2}}\,dx = \arcsin x + C$, since $D_x \arcsin x = \dfrac{1}{\sqrt{1-x^2}}$. (See $\int 36$, with $a = 1$.) An alternative answer, since
$D_x \arccos x = \dfrac{-1}{\sqrt{1-x^2}}$, is $-\arccos x + C$. Note that the arcsin and $-\arccos$ differ by a constant: $\arcsin x = \dfrac{\pi}{2} - \arccos x$.

19 $\int \sec x \tan x\,dx = \sec x + C$, since $D_x \sec x = \sec x \tan x$. (See $\int 66$.)

20 $\int \csc^2 x \, dx \,=\, ?$

21 $\displaystyle\int \frac{1}{1 + x^2} \, dx \,=\, ?$

The integral counterpart to the formula $D_x aF = aD_x F$ is

$$\int af(x) \, dx = a\int f(x) \, dx$$

For, if $F(x)$ is an antiderivative of $f(x)$, then $aF(x)$ is an antiderivative of $af(x)$.   Operationally, this permits the removal of a *constant factor* from the integrand of an indefinite integral.   It does *not* permit the removal of a nonconstant factor (see $\int 1$).

---

22 $\int 5 \cos x \, dx \,=\, ?$

23 $\int \tfrac{1}{2} \sin x \, dx \,=\, ?$

24 $\int 7x^3 \, dx \,=\, ?$

25 Criticize the following argument: $\int x \cdot x^3 \, dx = x\int x^3 \, dx = x\tfrac{1}{4}x^4 + C = \tfrac{1}{4}x^5 + C.$

The indefinite integral of the sum (difference) of two or more functions is the sum (difference) of the indefinite integrals of the functions

$$\int [f(x) \pm g(x)] \, dx = \int f(x) \, dx \pm \int g(x) \, dx$$

This follows from the corresponding theorem about derivatives (see $\int 2$).

---

26 $\int (x^2 + \cos x) \, dx \,=\, ?$

27 $\int (x^3 + 2x^2 + 5) \, dx \,=\, ?$

20 $\int \csc^2 x \, dx = -\cot x + C$, since $D_x(-\cot x) = -(-\csc^2 x) = \csc^2 x$
(See $\int 72$.)

21 $\arctan x + C$, since $D_x \arctan x = \dfrac{1}{1 + x^2}$.

22 $\int 5 \cos x \, dx = 5 \int \cos x \, dx = 5 \sin x + C$

23 $\int \frac{1}{2} \sin x \, dx = \frac{1}{2} \int \sin x \, dx = \frac{1}{2}(-\cos x) + C = -\frac{1}{2} \cos x + C$

24 $\int 7x^3 \, dx = 7 \int x^3 \, dx = 7\frac{1}{4}x^4 + C = \frac{7}{4}x^4 + C$

25 The first equality is false.   That $\int af(x) \, dx = a \int f(x) \, dx$ follows when a is a constant function.   It was here incorrectly applied to the identity function x.   We should have written

$\int xx^3 \, dx = \int x^4 \, dx = \frac{1}{5}x^5 + C.$

26 $\int (x^2 + \cos x) \, dx = \int x^2 \, dx + \int \cos x \, dx = \frac{1}{3}x^3 + \sin x + C.$ If   you wrote

$\int (x^2 + \cos x) \, dx = \int x^2 \, dx + \int \cos x \, dx = \frac{1}{3}x^3 + C_1 + \sin x + C_2$

this is also correct.   But note that the sum of the two constants $C_1 + C_2$ can be written as a single constant.

27 $\frac{1}{4}x^4 + \frac{2}{3}x^3 + 5x + C$

28 $\displaystyle\int \frac{x^3 + 2x^2 + 5}{x}\, dx = ?$

29 $\int (x + 3)(x - 3)\, dx = ?$

30 $\int (x^3 + 3)^2\, dx = ?$

31 $\displaystyle\int \frac{x^3 + 2x^2 - 5}{\sqrt{x}}\, dx = ?$

32 $\displaystyle\int \left(\sqrt{x} + \frac{1}{\sqrt{x}}\right)^2 dx = ?$

28   The integrand can be written as a sum

$$\frac{x^3 + 2x^2 + 5}{x} = x^2 + 2x + \frac{5}{x}.$$

Hence

$$\int \frac{x^3 + 2x^2 + 5}{x}\, dx = \int \left(x^2 + 2x + \frac{5}{x} \right) dx$$

$$= \int x^2\, dx + \int 2x\, dx + 5 \int \frac{1}{x}\, dx$$

$$= \tfrac{1}{3}x^3 + x^2 + 5 \ln x + C.$$

The derivative formulas related to products and quotients of functions are somewhat complicated; we would therefore expect the indefinite integrals of products and quotients to be messy. When convenient, it is desirable to write an integrand, which is represented as a product or as a quotient, as a sum.

29   The integrand is a product, but can be written as a difference: $x^2 - 9$. Thus

$$\int (x + 3)(x - 3)\, dx = \int (x^2 - 9)\, dx = \int x^2\, dx - \int 9\, dx = \tfrac{1}{3}x^3 - 9x + C.$$

30   The integrand is a product, but can be written as a sum. Hence,

$$\int (x^3 + 3)^2\, dx = \int (x^6 + 6x^3 + 9)\, dx = \tfrac{1}{7}x^7 + \tfrac{6}{4}x^4 + 9x + C.$$

31 $$\int \frac{x^3 + 2x^2 - 5}{\sqrt{x}}\, dx = \int (x^{\frac{5}{2}} + 2x^{\frac{3}{2}} - 5x^{-\frac{1}{2}})\, dx$$

$$= \tfrac{2}{7}x^{\frac{7}{2}} + \tfrac{4}{5}x^{\frac{5}{2}} - 10x^{\frac{1}{2}} + C$$

32 $$\int \left(\sqrt{x} + \frac{1}{\sqrt{x}} \right)^2 dx = \int \left(x + 2 + \frac{1}{x} \right) dx = \tfrac{1}{2}x^2 + 2x + \ln x + C$$

33 $\int (2x + 3)^5 \, dx = ?$

34 $\int (3x + 2)^{52} \, dx = ?$ Guess the answer, check by taking a derivative, and adjust your guess, if necessary.

35 $\displaystyle\int \frac{1}{3x + 2} \, dx = ?$ Guess this answer, check by taking a derivative, and adjust your guess, if necessary.

36 $\int (x^3 + 3)^2 \, dx = ?$ Guess the answer, check by taking a derivative. Why can't you adjust your guess in this case?

37 Is $\displaystyle\int \frac{1}{1 + x^2} \, dx = \ln (1 + x^2) + C$?

38 $\displaystyle\int \frac{1}{(5x - 3)^4} \, dx = ?$ Guess and check.

39 $\int (5x - 3)^{-1} \, dx = ?$ Guess and check.

40 $\int x(x - 3) \, dx = ?$

We recall the notation for the composition of two functions

$$f(u)|^{u=g(x)} = f[g(x)]$$

and here apply it to indefinite integrals.   For example, since $\int \cos u \, du = \sin u + C$, we write $\int \cos u \, du|^{u=x^2}$ to mean $\sin u + C|^{u=x^2} = \sin (x^2) + C$. In general, if $\int f(u) \, du = F(u) + C$, then

$$\int f(u) \, du|^{u=g(x)} = F(u) + C|^{u=g(x)} = F(g(x)) + C$$

33 We assume you first wrote $(2x + 3)^5$ as a sum: $32x^5 + 240x^4 + \cdots$, then integrated each term. Perhaps it is easier to *guess* an answer by using the power formula. Try

$$\int (2x + 3)^5\, dx = \tfrac{1}{6}(2x + 3)^6 + C$$

and check via derivatives.

$$D_x \tfrac{1}{6}(2x + 3)^6 = \tfrac{1}{6}6(2x + 3)^5 \cdot 2 = 2(2x + 3)^5$$

which contains the unwanted factor 2, introduced by the chain rule. It is not difficult to adjust our guess to allow for this constant factor and write

$$\int (2x + 3)^5\, dx = \tfrac{1}{12}\,(2x + 3)^6 + C$$

which checks out correctly. This kind of guessing will be fruitful when the integrand is a power of a *first*-degree polynomial.

34 $\tfrac{1}{159}(3x + 2)^{53} + C$

35 $\tfrac{1}{3}\ln(3x + 2) + C$

36 If you first guessed $\tfrac{1}{3}(x^3 + 3)^3$, then

$$D_x \tfrac{1}{3}(x^3 + 3)^3 = \tfrac{1}{3}3(x^3 + 3)^2 3x^2$$

which contains the unwanted factor $3x^2$ introduced by the chain rule. This nonconstant factor precludes a simple adjustment. Since the integrand is not a power of a first degree polynomial we are compelled to first write the integrand as a sum:

$$\int (x^3 + 3)^2\, dx = \int (x^6 + 6x^3 + 9)\, dx = \tfrac{1}{7}x^7 + \tfrac{3}{2}x^4 + 9x + C.$$

37 No. By the chain rule, $D_x \ln(1 + x^2) = \dfrac{1}{1 + x^2}\,(2x) \neq \dfrac{1}{1 + x^2}$.

$$\int \frac{1}{1 + x^2}\, dx = \arctan x + C$$

38 $-\tfrac{1}{15}\,(5x - 3)^{-3} + C$

39 $\tfrac{1}{5}\ln(5x - 3) + C$

40 $\displaystyle\int x(x - 3)\, dx = \int (x^2 - 3x)\, dx = \frac{x^3}{3} - \frac{3}{2}x^2 + C$

41 Evaluate $\int \cos u \, du \big|^{u=2x}$.

42 Evaluate $\int u^2 \, du \big|^{u=\sin x}$.

43 Evaluate $\displaystyle\int \frac{1}{u} \, du \Bigg|^{u=\sin x}$.

The first technique of integration introduced here, other than that of pure recognition, is called *change of variables*. It is the integration counterpart to the chain rule for derivatives and may be written as

$$\int f[g(x)]g'(x) \, dx = \int f(u) \, du \big|^{u=g(x)}$$

If $F(u)$ is an antiderivative of $f(u)$, then

$$\int f(u) \, du \big|^{u=g(x)} = F(u) + C \big|^{u=g(x)}$$

By the chain rule,

$$D_x[F(u) + C \big|^{u=g(x)}] = f(u) \cdot g'(x) \big|^{u=g(x)} = f[g(x)] \cdot g'(x)$$

and this shows that $\int f(u) \, du \big|^{u=g(x)}$ is an antiderivative of $f[g(x)] \cdot g'(x)$. Operationally we apply this result as follows:

1   Consider $\int f[g(x)] \cdot g'(x) \, dx$.

2   Replace $g(x)$ by a new variable u, and at the same time, *replace $g'(x) \, dx$ by du*, obtaining $\int f(u) \, du$.

3   Evaluate $\int f(u) \, du$, say $\int f(u) \, du = F(u) + C$.

4   Then $\int f[g(x)] \cdot g'(x) \, dx = \int f(u) \, du \big|^{u=g(x)}$
$$= F(u) + C \big|^{u=g(x)}$$
$$= F(g(x)) + C.$$

Given an indefinite integral $\int h(x) \, dx$ which the student is unable to evaluate by inspection. If he can discover, hiding in the integrand $h(x)$, a function $g(x)$ *whose derivative $g'(x)$ appears as a factor of $h(x)$*, then the procedure outlined above will lead to a second integral which he *may* be able to evaluate by inspection. This is a trial-and-error procedure; sometimes it works, sometimes it doesn't. The next few problems are artificially selected so as to succumb to a suitable change of variables.

41 Since $\int \cos u \, du = \sin u + C$,

$\int \cos u \, du|^{u=2x} = \sin u + C|^{u=2x} = \sin 2x + C$.

42 Since $\int u^2 \, du = \frac{1}{3}u^3 + C$,

$\int u^2 \, du|^{u=\sin x} = \frac{1}{3}u^3 + C|^{u=\sin x} = \frac{1}{3} \sin^3 x + C$.

43 Since $\displaystyle\int \frac{1}{u} \, du = \ln u + C$,

$\displaystyle\int \frac{1}{u} \, du\Big|^{u=\sin x} = \ln u + C|^{u=\sin x} = \ln (\sin x) + C$.

44 a Consider $\int (\sin x)^3 \cos x \, dx$. Can you find, hidden in the integrand, a function whose derivative appears as a factor of the integrand?

b In the symbol $\int (\sin x)^3 \cos x \, dx$, replace $\sin x$ by u and $\cos x \, dx$ by du to obtain ———.

c Evaluate $\int u^3 \, du$.

d Put Frame **44a**, **b**, and **c** together to evaluate $\int (\sin x)^3 \cos x \, dx$.

e Check Frame **44d** by differentiation.

45 a Consider $\int (\ln x) \dfrac{1}{x} \, dx$. Can you find, in the integrand, a function whose derivative appears as a factor of the integrand?

b In the symbol $\int (\ln x) \dfrac{1}{x} \, dx$, replace $\ln x$ by u and, correspondingly, $\dfrac{1}{x} \, dx$ by du to obtain ———.

c Evaluate $\int u \, du$.

d Put Frame **45a**, **b**, and **c** together to evaluate $\displaystyle\int \frac{\ln x}{x} \, dx$.

This change-of-variable technique, illustrated in Frames **44** and **45**, requires the identification of some function $g(x)$ in the integrand whose derivative $g'(x)$ appears as a *factor* of the integrand. We replace $g(x)$ by a new variable u [we write $u = g(x)$], and *must* correspondingly replace $g'(x) \, dx$ by du [we write $du = g'(x) \, dx$]. Once the function $u = g(x)$ has been selected, we *must* replace du for $g'(x) \, dx$. If the derivative $g'(x)$ does not appear as a factor of the integrand, the method fails.

44 a The function $\sin x$ appears in the integrand, and its derivative $\cos x$ appears as a factor of the integrand.

b $\int u^3 \, du$

c $\int u^3 \, du = \frac{1}{4} u^4 + C$

d $\int (\sin x)^3 \cos x \, dx = \int u^3 \, du|^{u=\sin x} = \frac{1}{4} u^4 + C|^{u=\sin x} = \frac{1}{4} \sin^4 x + C$

e $D_x \frac{1}{4} \sin^4 x = \frac{1}{4} 4 \sin^3 x \cos x = \sin^3 x \cos x$

45 a The function $\ln x$ appears in the integrand, and its derivative $1/x$ appears as a factor of the integrand.

b $\int u \, du$

c $\int u \, du = \frac{1}{2} u^2 + C$

d $\displaystyle \int (\ln x) \frac{1}{x} \, dx = \int u \, du \Big|^{u=\ln x} = \frac{1}{2} u^2 + C|^{u=\ln x} = \frac{1}{2} (\ln x)^2 + C$

46 a Consider $\int \dfrac{e^x}{1+e^x}\, dx$. Can you find in the integrand a function whose derivative appears as a factor of the integrand? Let u replace this function. What must du then replace?

b Let $u = 1 + e^x$, and proceed to evaluate $\int \dfrac{e^x}{1+e^x}\, dx$.

47 a Consider $\int \tan^3 x \sec^2 x\, dx$. Can you find in the integrand a function whose derivative appears as a factor of the integrand? Let u replace this function. What must du replace?

b Replace $\tan x$ by u and proceed to evaluate $\int \tan^3 x \sec^2 x\, dx$.

c Apply the same method to evaluate

$\int \tan^9 x \sec^2 x\, dx \qquad$ and $\qquad \int (\tan x)^{-1} \sec^2 x\, dx$.

48 a Consider $\int \dfrac{2x+3}{x^2+3x+5}\, dx$. Can you find in the integrand a function whose derivative appears as a factor of the integrand? Let u replace this function. What must du replace?

b Replace $(x^2 + 3x + 5)$ by u and proceed to evaluate the integral $\int \dfrac{2x+3}{x^2+3x+5}\, dx$.

46 **a** We could let $u = e^x$, then $du = e^x\,dx$ and

$$\int \frac{e^x}{1 + e^x}\,dx = \int \frac{1}{1 + e^x}\,e^x\,dx = \int \frac{1}{1 + u}\,du\Big|^{u=e^x}.$$

However, we could instead let $u = 1 + e^x$; then $du = e^x\,dx$ and

$$\int \frac{1}{1 + e^x}\,e^x\,dx = \int \frac{1}{u}\,du\Big|^{u=1+e^x}$$

and, since this last integral is simpler than the one obtained above, we proceed with this.

b Let $u = 1 + e^x$, $du = e^x\,dx$. Thus,

$$\int \frac{1}{1 + e^x}\,e^x\,dx = \int \frac{1}{u}\,du\Big|^{u=1+e^x}$$
$$= \ln u + C\big|^{u=1+e^x} = \ln(1 + e^x) + C.$$

47 **a** $u = \tan x \qquad du = \sec^2 x\,dx$

b Let $u = \tan x$, $du = \sec^2 x\,dx$.
$$\int \tan^3 x \sec^2 x\,dx = \int u^3\,du\big|^{u=\tan x}$$
$$= \tfrac{1}{4}u^4 + C\big|^{u=\tan x} = \tfrac{1}{4}\tan^4 x + C$$

c Let $u = \tan x$, $du = \sec^2 x\,dx$.
$$\int \tan^9 x \sec^2 x\,dx = \int u^9\,du\big|^{u=\tan x}$$
$$= \tfrac{1}{10}u^{10} + C\big|^{u=\tan x} = \tfrac{1}{10}\tan^{10} x + C$$
$$\int (\tan x)^{-1} \sec^2 x\,dx = \int u^{-1}\,du\big|^{u=\tan x}$$
$$= \ln u + C\big|^{u=\tan x} = \ln(\tan x) + C$$

48 **a** $u = x^2 + 3x + 5 \qquad du = (2x + 3)\,dx$

b $\displaystyle \int \frac{1}{x^2 + 3x + 5}\,(2x + 3)\,dx = \int \frac{1}{u}\,du$
$$= \ln u + C\big|^{u=(x^2+3x+5)}$$
$$= \ln(x^2 + 3x + 5) + C$$

Note that this method would fail if the numerator of the integrand were changed slightly, say to $(2x + 4)$.

49 a Consider $\int \dfrac{x}{1+x^2}\,dx$. Can you find in the integrand a function whose derivative appears as a factor of the integrand?

b Let $u = 1 + x^2$ and proceed to evaluate the integral $\int \dfrac{x}{1+x^2}\,dx$.

50 Evaluate $\int \dfrac{x}{\sqrt{1-x^2}}\,dx$ by replacing $(1 - x^2)$ by u.

51 $\int \dfrac{x^2}{x^3+4}\,dx = \ ?$

49 a Not quite. The derivative of $(1 + x^2)$ is $2x$. However if we rewrite the integrand in equivalent algebraic form:

$$\frac{x}{1 + x^2} = \frac{1}{2} \cdot \frac{1}{1 + x^2} \cdot 2x$$

then the derivative of $(1 + x^2)$ does appear as a factor of the integrand.

b Let $u = 1 + x^2$. Then $du = 2x\,dx$ and

$$\int \frac{x}{1 + x^2}\,dx = \int \frac{1}{2} \cdot \frac{1}{1 + x^2} \cdot 2x\,dx = \int \frac{1}{2} \cdot \frac{1}{u}\,du$$

$$= \frac{1}{2} \int \frac{1}{u}\,du = \frac{1}{2}\ln u + C\big|_{u=1+x^2}$$

$$= \tfrac{1}{2}\ln(1 + x^2) + C.$$

This problem illustrates that the integrand can be adjusted algebraically to provide a missing *constant* factor.

50 Let $u = 1 - x^2$, $du = -2x\,dx$. Adjust the integrand by multiplying it by $(-\frac{1}{2})(-2) = 1$.

$$\int (1 - x^2)^{-\frac{1}{2}}x\,dx = -\tfrac{1}{2}\int (1 - x^2)^{-\frac{1}{2}}(-2x)\,dx$$
$$= -\tfrac{1}{2}\int u^{-\frac{1}{2}}\,du = -\tfrac{1}{2}2u^{\frac{1}{2}} + C\big|_{u=1-x^2}$$
$$= -\sqrt{1 - x^2} + C$$

51 Let $u = x^3 + 4$, then $du = 3x^2\,dx$.

$$\int \frac{x^2}{x^3 + 4}\,dx = \frac{1}{3}\int \frac{1}{x^3 + 4}\,3x^2\,dx$$

$$= \frac{1}{3}\int \frac{1}{u}\,du = \frac{1}{3}\ln u + C\big|_{u=x^3+4}$$

$$= \frac{1}{3}\ln(x^3 + 4) + C$$

52　**a**　$\int e^{ax}\,dx = ?$　　$(a$ is a constant $\neq 0)$

　　b　Apply ∫95 to evaluate $\int e^{2x}\,dx.$

　　c　Apply ∫95 to evaluate $\int e^{-x}\,dx.$

53　**a**　$\int \sin^m x \cos x\,dx = ?$　　$(m \neq -1)$

　　b　Apply ∫65 to evaluate $\displaystyle\int \frac{\cos x}{\sin^3 x}\,dx.$

　　c　Apply ∫65 to evaluate $\int \sin x \cos x\,dx.$

52 **a** Let $u = ax$, then $du = a\,dx$.

$$\int e^{ax}\,dx = \frac{1}{a}\int e^{ax}a\,dx = \frac{1}{a}\int e^u\,du\Big|^{u=ax}$$

$$= \frac{1}{a}e^u + C\Big|_{u=ax} = \frac{e^{ax}}{a} + C$$

b With a replaced by 2, $\displaystyle\int e^{2x}\,dx = \frac{e^{2x}}{2} + C.$

c With a replaced by -1,

$$\int e^{-x}\,dx = \frac{e^{-x}}{-1} + C = -e^{-x} + C. \qquad \text{(See also } \smallint 94.)$$

53 **a** Let $u = \sin x$, then $du = \cos x\,dx$.

$$\int \sin^m x \cos x\,dx = \int u^m\,du\Big|^{u=\sin x} = \frac{u^{m+1}}{m+1} + C\Big|^{u=\sin x}$$

$$= \frac{\sin^{m+1} x}{m+1} + C \qquad \text{(See } \smallint 65)$$

b Replace m by -3, thus

$$\int \frac{\cos x}{\sin^3 x}\,dx = \int \sin^{-3} x \cos x\,dx$$

$$= \frac{(\sin x)^{-2}}{-2} + C = \frac{-1}{2\sin^2 x} + C.$$

c Replace m by 1.

$$\int \sin^1 x \cos x\,dx = \frac{\sin^2 x}{2} + C \qquad \text{(See } \smallint 62)$$

d Apply ∫65 to evaluate $\displaystyle\int \frac{\cos x}{\sin^2 x}\,dx.$

e $\int \cos^m x \sin x \, dx = ?$

54 a $\displaystyle\int \frac{\cos x}{\sin x}\,dx = ?$

b $\int \cot x \, dx = ?$ (See Frame **54a**)

c $\int \tan x \, dx = \displaystyle\int \frac{\sin x}{\cos x}\,dx = ?$

55 a $\int \sec^3 x \sec x \tan x \, dx = ?$

b $\int \sec^4 x \tan x \, dx = ?$

c Rewrite the integrand in terms of sines and cosines, then apply ∫64 to evaluate ∫ sec⁴ x tan x dx.

d Replace m by -2.

$$\int \frac{\cos x}{\sin^2 x} \, dx = \frac{(\sin x)^{-1}}{-1} + C = -\csc x + C$$

Note also that the integral can be written as $\int \cot x \csc x \, dx$ and evaluated by recognition.

e Let $u = \cos x$, $du = -\sin x \, dx$.

$$\int \cos^m x \sin x \, dx = \frac{-\cos^{m+1} x}{m + 1} + C \qquad \text{(See } \int 64)$$

54 a Let $u = \sin x$, then $du = \cos x \, dx$.

$$\int \frac{\cos x}{\sin x} \, dx = \int \frac{1}{u} \, du \Big|^{u=\sin x}$$
$$= \ln u + C \big|_{u=\sin x} = \ln (\sin x) + C$$

b $\displaystyle \int \cot x \, dx = \int \frac{\cos x}{\sin x} \, dx = \ln (\sin x) + C \qquad \text{(See } \int 48)$

c Let $u = \cos x$, then $du = -\sin x \, dx$.

$$\int \tan x \, dx = - \int \frac{1}{\cos x} (-\sin x) \, dx$$
$$= - \int \frac{1}{u} \, du = -\ln u + C \Big|^{u=\cos x}$$
$$= -\ln \cos x + C \qquad \text{(See } \int 47)$$

55 a Let $u = \sec x$, then $du = \sec x \tan x \, dx$.

$$\int \sec^3 x \sec x \tan x \, dx = \int u^3 \, du = \tfrac{1}{4} u^4 + C \Big|^{u=\sec x} = \frac{\sec^4 x}{4} + C$$

b This is the same problem as Frame **55a**. By writing $\sec^4 x \tan x$ as $\sec^3 x \cdot (\sec x \tan x)$ we recognize a function $\sec x$ whose derivative appears as a factor of the integrand.

c $\displaystyle \int \sec^4 x \tan x \, dx = \int \sin x \cos^{-5} x \, dx$

$$= - \frac{\cos^{-4} x}{-4} + C = \tfrac{1}{4} \sec^4 x + C$$

56 **a** $\displaystyle\int \frac{\sec^2 x + \sec x \tan x}{\sec x + \tan x}\, dx = ?$ Can you find in the integrand a function whose derivative appears as a factor of the integrand?

b $\int \sec x \, dx = ?$ This is tricky. Note that

$$\sec x = \frac{\sec^2 x + \sec x \tan x}{\sec x + \tan x}$$

Thus by Frame **56a**,

$\int \sec x \, dx = \ln\,(\sec x + \tan x) + C$ (see ∫49).

c Show that $\csc x = \dfrac{\csc^2 x - \csc x \cot x}{\csc x - \cot x}$ and note that the numerator of the fraction is the derivative of the denominator. Then evaluate $\int \csc x \, dx$.

57 **a** $\int \cos 3x \, dx = ?$

b $\int \sin^m 3x \cos 3x \, dx = ?$ $(m \neq -1)$

58 $\int \sec (x^2 + 1) \tan (x^2 + 1)\, x \, dx = ?$

56 **a** Let $u = \sec x + \tan x$, then $du = (\sec x \tan x + \sec^2 x)\, dx$.

$$\int \frac{\sec^2 x + \sec x \tan x}{\sec x + \tan x}\, dx = \int \frac{1}{u}\, du$$
$$= \ln u + C\,|u=\sec x + \tan x$$
$$= \ln (\sec x + \tan x) + C$$

b Proceed to Frame **56c**.

c Let $u = \csc x - \cot x$, then $du = (\csc^2 x - \csc x \cot x)\, dx$.

$$\int \csc x\, dx = \int \frac{\csc^2 x - \csc x \cot x}{\csc x - \cot x}\, dx = \int \frac{1}{u}\, du$$
$$= \ln u + C\,|u=\csc x - \cot x$$
$$= \ln (\csc x - \cot x) + C \qquad \text{(See } \int 50)$$

The formulas $\int 49$ and $\int 50$ will be used repeatedly in the sequel. They need not be memorized, but their existence must be known to the student.

57 **a** Let $u = 3x$, then $du = 3\, dx$.

$$\int \cos 3x\, dx = \tfrac{1}{3}\int \cos 3x\; 3\, dx = \tfrac{1}{3}\int \cos u\, du$$
$$= \tfrac{1}{3} \sin u + C\,|u=3x = \tfrac{1}{3} \sin 3x + C$$

The student could have perhaps evaluated this integral by recognition.

b Let $u = 3x$, then $du = 3\, dx$.

$$\int \sin^m 3x \cos 3x\, dx = \tfrac{1}{3}\int \sin^m 3x \cos 3x\; 3\, dx$$
$$= \tfrac{1}{3}\int \sin^m u \cos u\, du\,|u=3x$$
$$= \text{(and then apply } \int 65 \text{ or the method of}$$
$$\text{Frame } \mathbf{53})$$
$$= \frac{\sin^{m+1} u}{3(m+1)} + C\,|u=3x = \frac{\sin^{m+1} 3x}{3(m+1)} + C$$

58 Let $u = x^2 + 1$, then $du = 2x\, dx$.

$$\int \sec (x^2 + 1) \tan (x^2 + 1) x\, dx = \tfrac{1}{2}\int \sec (x^2 + 1) \tan (x^2 + 1)\, 2x\, dx$$
$$= \tfrac{1}{2}\int \sec u \tan u\, du$$
$$= \tfrac{1}{2} \sec u + C\,|u=x^2+1$$
$$= \tfrac{1}{2} \sec (x^2 + 1) + C$$

59 $\int x \sin 5x^2 \, dx = ?$

60 $\int \csc^2 \dfrac{x}{3} \, dx = ?$

61 $\displaystyle\int \tan \dfrac{x}{3} \, dx = ?$ Remember that the "trick" for integrating the tangent function is to write $\tan u = \dfrac{\sin u}{\cos u}$.

62 $\int \sqrt{\sin 3x} \cos 3x \, dx = ?$

59 Let $u = 5x^2$, then $du = 10x\,dx$.

$$\int x \sin 5x^2 \, dx = \tfrac{1}{10} \int (\sin 5x^2) \, 10x \, dx$$
$$= \tfrac{1}{10} \int \sin u \, du = -\tfrac{1}{10} \cos u + C \big|^{u=5x^2}$$
$$= -\tfrac{1}{10} \cos 5x^2 + C$$

Note that the apparently simpler problem $\int \sin 5x^2 \, dx$ would not succumb by this method. The derivative of $5x^2$ does not appear as a factor of the integrand.

60 Let $u = \dfrac{x}{3} = \dfrac{1}{3}\,x$, then $du = \dfrac{1}{3}\,dx$.

$$\int \csc^2 \frac{x}{3} \, dx = 3 \int \csc^2 u \, du = -3 \cot u + C \big|^{u=x/3} = -3 \cot \frac{x}{3} + C$$

61 If you let $u = \dfrac{x}{3}$, thus $du = \dfrac{1}{3}\,dx$, you will first obtain

$$\int \tan \frac{x}{3} \, dx = 3 \int \tan u \, du$$

and the problem is resolved by the evaluation of $\int \tan u \, du$ (see $\int 47$).

However, we can first write: $\tan \dfrac{x}{3} = \dfrac{\sin \dfrac{x}{3}}{\cos \dfrac{x}{3}}$ and let $v = \cos \dfrac{x}{3}$; then

$$dv = -\left(\sin \frac{x}{3}\right) \frac{1}{3} \, dx.$$

$$\int \tan \frac{x}{3} \, dx = -3 \int \frac{1}{\cos (x/3)} \left(-\sin \frac{x}{3}\right) \frac{1}{3} \, dx = -3 \int \frac{1}{v} \, dv$$
$$= -3 \ln v + C \big|^{v=\cos \,(x/3)} = -3 \ln \cos \frac{x}{3} + C.$$

62 Let $u = \sin 3x$, then $du = (\cos 3x) \, 3 \, dx$.

$$\int \sqrt{\sin 3x} \, \cos 3x \, dx = \tfrac{1}{3} \int \sqrt{\sin 3x} \, (\cos 3x) \, 3 \, dx = \tfrac{1}{3} \int u^{\frac{1}{2}} \, du$$
$$= \tfrac{2}{9} u^{\frac{3}{2}} + C \big|^{u=\sin 3x} = \tfrac{2}{9} (\sin 3x)^{\frac{3}{2}} + C$$

63 **a** $\int \sin (a + bx) \, dx = ?$ $(b \neq 0)$

   b $\int \cos (a + bx) \, dx = ?$ $(b \neq 0)$

   c Apply $\int 58$ to evaluate $\int \cos \dfrac{x}{3} \, dx$.

63 a Let $u = a + bx$, then $du = b\ dx$.

$$\int \sin (a + bx)\ dx = \frac{1}{b} \int \sin (a + bx)\ b\ dx = \frac{1}{b} \int \sin u\ du$$

$$= -\frac{1}{b} \cos u + C\Big|_{u=a+bx}$$

$$= -\frac{1}{b} \cos (a + bx) + C \qquad (\text{See } \textstyle\int 57)$$

b Let $u = a + bx$, then $du = b\ dx$.

$$\int \cos (a + bx)\ dx = \frac{1}{b} \int \cos (a + bx)\ b\ dx$$

$$= \frac{1}{b} \int \cos u\ du \Big|_{u=a+bx} = \frac{1}{b} \sin u + C \Big|_{u=a+bx}$$

$$= \frac{1}{b} \sin (a + bx) + C \qquad (\text{See } \textstyle\int 58)$$

c Replace a by 0 and b by $\frac{1}{3}$; obtain $3 \sin \dfrac{x}{3} + C$.

All properties of indefinite integrals follow from corresponding properties of derivatives. We say, for example, $\int \cos x \, dx = \sin x + C$ because $D_x \sin x = \cos x$. That the integral of the sum of two functions is the sum of their integrals follows from the corresponding theorem on derivatives. The *change-of-variable* technique for integration is justified by the *chain rule* for derivatives. We now present a formula called *integration by parts* which is justified by the *product formula* for derivatives. If u is a function, $u = u(x)$, we continue to write $du = u'(x) \, dx$. Let u and v be functions; then $D_x(u \cdot v) = u(x)v'(x) + v(x)u'(x)$. This leads to the integral formulas (we omit the constant C)

$$u \cdot v = \int [u(x)v'(x) + v(x)u'(x)] \, dx$$
$$u \cdot v = \int u(x)v'(x) \, dx + \int v(x)u'(x) \, dx$$
$$u \cdot v = \int u \, dv + \int v \, du$$

(1) $$\int u \, dv = u \cdot v - \int v \, du$$

This last formula (1) is called *integration by parts*. It is useful in cases where an integral of the form $\int u \, dv$ is to be evaluated and an antiderivative is not recognized, but, for the same functions u and v, the integral $\int v \, du$ is accessible.

64 a Let $u = x$ and $v = \sin x$ and write the instance of the integration-by-parts formula determined by these functions.

b Apply Frame **64a** to evaluate $\int x \cos x \, dx$.

c Find a function v such that $dv = \sin x \, dx$.

d Consider $\int x \sin x \, dx$. Let $u = x$ and $dv = \sin x \, dx$. Note that the given integral is of the form $\int u \, dv$. Find the corresponding $du = ? \; v = ?$ and evaluate the integral by integration by parts.

e Consider $\int x e^x \, dx$. Let $u = e^x$ and $dv = x \, dx$. Note that the given integral is of the form $\int u \, dv$. Find the corresponding $du = ? \; v = ?$ and write the instance of the integration-by-parts formula determined by these functions.

f Consider again $\int x e^x \, dx$. Let $u = x$ and $dv = e^x \, dx$. Note that the given integral is of the form $\int u \, dv$. Find the corresponding $du = ? \; v = ?$ and proceed to evaluate the integral by integration by parts.

64 **a** Since $u = x$ and $v = \sin x$, then $du = 1\, dx$ and $dv = \cos x\, dx$. Replacing these in $\int u\, dv = uv - \int v\, du$, we obtain

$\int x \cos x\, dx = x \sin x - \int \sin x\, dx$.

b $\int x \cos x\, dx = x \sin x + \cos x + C$. (See $\int 77$.) Note that for these functions, $\int u\, dv = \int x \cos x\, dx$ is not in recognizable form, but $\int v\, du = \int \sin x\, dx$ can be evaluated by inspection.

c The answer is not unique. One such function is $-\cos x$, since, if $v = -\cos x$, then $dv = \sin x\, dx$. Of course, for any constant C, $-\cos x + C$ is also such a function. The procedure "given dv, find v" will of necessity occur in every application of integration by parts. This is itself an integration procedure, but here we seek only one of the antiderivatives.

d $\begin{cases} u = x \\ dv = \sin x\, dx \end{cases} \quad \begin{cases} du = 1\, dx \\ v = -\cos x \end{cases}$

$\int x \sin x\, dx = \int u\, dv = uv - \int v\, du = -x \cos x + \int \cos x\, dx$
$\qquad\qquad\quad = -x \cos x + \sin x + C \qquad \text{(See } \int 73\text{)}$

e $\begin{cases} u = e^x \\ dv = x\, dx \end{cases} \quad \begin{cases} du = e^x\, dx \\ v = \frac{1}{2}x^2 \end{cases}$

$\int xe^x\, dx = \int u\, dv = uv - \int v\, du$
$\qquad\quad = \frac{1}{2}x^2 e^x - \frac{1}{2}\int x^2 e^x\, dx$

The integral in the last line looks more complicated than the integral we are attempting to evaluate. We abandon this approach to the problem.

f $\begin{cases} u = x \\ dv = e^x\, dx \end{cases} \quad \begin{cases} du = 1\, dx \\ v = e^x \end{cases}$

$\int xe^x\, dx = \int u\, dv = uv - \int v\, du = xe^x - \int e^x\, dx$
$\qquad\quad = xe^x - e^x + C = (x - 1)e^x + C$

(See $\int 96$ with a replaced by 1.) The integrands of the last few problems were $x \cos x$, $x \sin x$, xe^x. Note that each of them is a product of two relatively immiscible functions, a polynomial and a trigonometric function, a polynomial and an exponential function. This is an environment in which integration by parts is indicated.

65 a Consider $\int \ln x\, dx$. Can you evaluate this readily by inspection?

   b Write $\int \ln x\, dx$ in the form $\int u\, dv$; that is, write $u\ =\ ?\ dv\ =\ ?$ such that $\int \ln x\, dx\ =\ \int u\, dv$.

   c Evaluate $\int \ln x\, dx$.

66 $\int x \ln x\, dx\ =\ ?$

67 a $\int x^p \ln x\, dx\ =\ ?$ $(p \neq -1)$

   b Show that $\int 89$ is an instance of $\int 90$.

65 a No. We hope, at this stage, that you did not write

$$\int \ln x \, dx = \frac{1}{x} + C.$$

We are not finding a derivative of $\ln x$; we seek a function whose derivative is $\ln x$.

b This can be done in two ways: (1) $u = 1$, $dv = \ln x \, dx$, or (2) $u = \ln x$, and $dv = 1 \, dx$. The first of these is useless, since the problem of finding a function v such that $dv = \ln x \, dx$ is equivalent to the original problem. If we knew such a function, we could evaluate the original integral $\int \ln x \, dx$ by inspection.

c
$$\begin{cases} u = \ln x \\ dv = 1 \, dx \end{cases} \quad \begin{cases} du = \frac{1}{x} \, dx \\ v = x \end{cases}$$

$$\int \ln x \, dx = \int u \, dv = uv - \int v \, du = x \ln x - \int 1 \, dx$$
$$= x \ln x - x + C \qquad \text{(See } \int 87\text{)}$$

66
$$\begin{cases} u = \ln x \\ dv = x \, dx \end{cases} \quad \begin{cases} du = \frac{1}{x} \, dx \\ v = \frac{1}{2}x^2 \end{cases}$$

The other natural choice for u and dv leads to a more complicated integral $\int v \, du$.

$$\int x \ln x \, dx = \int u \, dv = uv - \int v \, du = \frac{1}{2}x^2 \ln x - \frac{1}{2}\int x \, dx$$
$$= \frac{1}{2}x^2 \ln x - \frac{1}{4}x^2 + C \qquad \text{(See } \int 88\text{)}$$

67 a
$$\text{Let} \begin{cases} u = \ln x \\ dv = x^p \, dx \end{cases} \quad \begin{cases} du = \frac{1}{x} \, dx \\ v = \dfrac{x^{p+1}}{p+1} \end{cases}$$

$$\int x^p \ln x \, dx = \int u \, dv = uv - \int v \, du$$

$$= \frac{x^{p+1}}{p+1} \ln x - \frac{1}{p+1} \int x^p \, dx$$

$$= \frac{x^{p+1}}{p+1} \ln x - \frac{x^{p+1}}{(p+1)^2} + C$$

(See $\int 90$, a replaced by 1)

b Let $p = 2$, $a = 1$.
$$\int x^2 \ln x \, dx = \frac{x^3}{3} \ln x - \frac{x^3}{9} + C.$$

68 $\int \arcsin x \, dx \; = \; ?$

69 $\int \arctan x \, dx \; = \; ?$

68

Let $\begin{cases} u = \arcsin x \\ dv = 1 \, dx \end{cases}$ $\begin{cases} du = \dfrac{1}{\sqrt{1 - x^2}} \, dx \\ v = x \end{cases}$

The other natural choice for u and dv is useless, for if $dv = \arcsin x \, dx$, the finding of the function v is equivalent to evaluating the given integral.

(1) $\displaystyle \int \arcsin x \, dx = x \arcsin x - \int \frac{x}{\sqrt{1 - x^2}} \, dx$

The integral on the right looks somewhat complicated but will succumb to a change-of-variable procedure. Let $w = 1 - x^2$; then $dw = -2x \, dx$ and

$$\int \frac{x}{\sqrt{1 - x^2}} \, dx = -\frac{1}{2} \int w^{-\frac{1}{2}} \, dw$$

$$= -w^{\frac{1}{2}} + C \Big|_{w = 1 - x^2} = -\sqrt{1 - x^2} + C.$$

Substituting this in (1), we obtain

$\int \arcsin x \, dx = x \arcsin x + \sqrt{1 - x^2} + C.$

(See $\int 81$. Almost the identical procedure will give $\int 82$, $\int 84$, $\int 85$.)

69

Let $\begin{cases} u = \arctan x \\ dv = 1 \, dx \end{cases}$ then $\begin{cases} du = \dfrac{1}{1 + x^2} \, dx \\ v = x \end{cases}$

$\displaystyle \int \arctan x \, dx = x \arctan x - \int \frac{x}{1 + x^2} \, dx$

Now, let $w = 1 + x^2$; then $dw = 2x \, dx$ and

$$\int \frac{x}{1 + x^2} \, dx = \frac{1}{2} \int \frac{1}{w} \, dw$$

$$= \tfrac{1}{2} \ln w + C \Big|_{w = 1 + x^2} = \tfrac{1}{2} \ln (1 + x^2) + C.$$

Hence, $\int 83$. With slight alteration we have $\int 86$.

Sometimes integration by parts must be applied more than once. For example, consider $\int x^2 e^x \, dx$. A single application of integration by parts (with $u = x^2$, $dv = e^x \, dx$; $du = 2x \, dx$, $v = e^x$) gives

$$\int x^2 e^x \, dx = x^2 e^x - 2 \int x e^x \, dx$$

The last integral appearing is itself not integrable by inspection, but may be evaluated by an application of integration by parts (with $u = x$, $dv = e^x \, dx$; $du = dx$, $v = e^x$):

$$\int x e^x \, dx = x e^x - \int e^x \, dx = x e^x - e^x + C$$

Combining these two results, with $C_1 = 2C$,

$$\int x^2 e^x \, dx = x^2 e^x - 2x e^x + 2e^x + C_1$$

70 a Show that $\int 97$ results from a single application of integration by parts.

   b Apply $\int 97$ to evaluate $\int x e^{3x} \, dx$.

   c Apply $\int 97$ several times to evaluate $\int x^3 e^x \, dx$.

71 a Formula $\int 76$ is another reduction formula. Show that it is obtained from a single application of integration by parts.

   b Apply $\int 76$ and $\int 80$ to derive, in turn, $\int 73$, $\int 78$, and $\int 75$.

70 **a** Let $\begin{cases} u = x^m \\ dv = e^{ax}\,dx \end{cases}$ $\begin{cases} du = mx^{m-1}\,dx \\ v = \dfrac{1}{a}\,e^{ax} \end{cases}$

$$\int x^m e^{ax}\,dx = \frac{x^m e^{ax}}{a} - \frac{m}{a}\int x^{m-1} e^{ax}\,dx$$

b Replace m by 1 and a by 3.

$$\int xe^{3x}\,dx = \frac{xe^{3x}}{3} - \frac{1}{3}\int e^{3x}\,dx = \frac{xe^{3x}}{3} - \frac{1}{9}e^{3x} + C$$

c $\int x^3 e^x\,dx = x^3 e^x - 3\int x^2 e^x\,dx$ $(a = 1,\ m = 3)$
$\int x^2 e^x\,dx = x^2 e^x - 2\int x^1 e^x\,dx$ $(m = 2)$
$\int xe^x\,dx = x^1 e^x - \int e^x\,dx = xe^x - e^x$ $(m = 1)$

Hence

$\int x^3 e^x\,dx = x^3 e^x - 3[x^2 e^x - 2(xe^x - e^x)] + C$
$\qquad = x^3 e^x - 3x^2 e^x + 6xe^x - 6e^x + C.$

A formula like $\int$97 is called a *reduction* formula—note that the power of x appearing in the integrand of the first integral is reduced in the resulting integral. Successive applications of such a formula lead to an integral which does not contain x as a factor $(x^0 = 1)$.

71 **a** Let $\begin{cases} u = x^m \\ dv = \sin x\,dx \end{cases}$ then $\begin{cases} du = mx^{m-1}\,dx \\ v = -\cos x \end{cases}$

Formula $\int$80 is a similar reduction formula.

b For $\int$73, let $m = 1$ in $\int$76. For $\int$78, let $m = 2$ in $\int$80; then apply $\int$73. For $\int$75, let $m = 3$ in $\int$76; then apply $\int$78. The sequence of formulas $\int$77, $\int$74, and $\int$79 is similarly derived.

72 a Consider now $\int e^x \sin x \, dx$. Let $u = e^x$ and $dv = \sin x \, dx$ and write this instance of the by-parts formula.

b The integral on the right in Frame **72a** is no simpler than the integral on the left. Let's see what results from a second application of integration by parts. Consider $\int \cos x \, e^x \, dx$; let $u = \cos x$ and $dv = e^x \, dx$. Write this instance of the by-parts formula, and substitute this into Eq. (1) in Frame **72a**.

c Consider $\int \cos x \cdot e^x \, dx$, $u = e^x$, and $dv = \cos x \, dx$. Apply the by-parts formula to this integral, then substitute into Eq. (1) in Frame **72a**:

$$\int e^x \sin x \, dx = -e^x \cos x + \int \cos x \cdot e^x \, dx.$$

d Solve Eq. (3) in Frame **72c** for $\int e^x \sin x \, dx$.

e Substitute Eq. (1) of Frame **72a** into Eq. (2) of Frame **72c** then solve, algebraically, the resulting equation in order to evaluate $\int e^x \cos x \, dx$.

73 $\displaystyle\int \frac{1}{x} (\ln x)^n \, dx = ?$

Flexibility in evaluating trigonometric integrals results from applying certain trigonometric identities. We here take a short interlude to review and recall a few useful identities.

(1) $\sin (x \pm y) = \sin x \cos y \pm \cos x \sin y$
(2) $\cos (x \pm y) = \cos x \cos y \mp \sin x \sin y$

Since $\cos 0 = 1$ and $\cos 0 = \cos (x - x)$, we obtain from (2) the well-known Pythagorean identity:

(3) $\cos^2 x + \sin^2 x = 1$ $\sin^2 x = 1 - \cos^2 x$ $\cos^2 x = 1 - \sin^2 x$

If we divide both sides of (3) by $\cos^2 x$, we obtain another useful Pythagorean identity:

(4) $1 + \tan^2 x = \sec^2 x$ $\tan^2 x = \sec^2 x - 1$

72 a With $\begin{cases} u = e^x \\ dv = \sin x \, dx \end{cases}$ then $\begin{cases} du = e^x \, dx \\ v = -\cos x \end{cases}$

(1) $\int e^x \sin x \, dx = -e^x \cos x + \int \cos x \cdot e^x \, dx$

b $\begin{cases} u = \cos x \\ dv = e^x \, dx \end{cases}$ $\begin{cases} du = -\sin x \, dx \\ v = e^x \end{cases}$.

$\int \cos x \cdot e^x \, dx = e^x \cos x + \int e^x \sin x \, dx$

$\int e^x \sin x \, dx = -e^x \cos x + (e^x \cos x + \int e^x \sin x \, dx)$

This last equation is equivalent to

$\int e^x \sin x \, dx = \int e^x \sin x \, dx$

which is true but not very useful. Our second application of integration by parts merely undid what was done in the first application. In the first application we let u equal the *exponential* function $u = e^x$, and we should have continued in this same vein in the second application.

c $\begin{cases} u = e^x \\ dv = \cos x \, dx \end{cases}$ $\begin{cases} du = e^x \, dx \\ v = \sin x \end{cases}$

(2) $\int \cos x \cdot e^x \, dx = e^x \sin x - \int e^x \sin x \, dx$

Substituting this into (1), we have

(3) $\int e^x \sin x \, dx = -e^x \cos x + e^x \sin x - \int e^x \sin x \, dx.$

d $2\int e^x \sin x \, dx = e^x \sin x - e^x \cos x$
$\int e^x \sin x \, dx = \frac{1}{2}(e^x \sin x - e^x \cos x)$

We have found one antiderivative of $e^x \sin x$; all others are obtained by adding some constant to it. (See $\int 98$ with a and p replaced by 1.)

e $\int e^x \cos x \, dx = \frac{1}{2}(e^x \sin x + e^x \cos x) + C$ (See $\int 99$)

73 You could obtain $\dfrac{1}{n+1} (\ln x)^{n+1} + C$ by applying the integration-by-parts procedure. However, note in the integrand, the function $\ln x$ whose derivative $\dfrac{1}{x}$ appears as a factor of the integrand. Thus the change-of-variable procedure may be applicable. (See $\int 91$.)

Since $\cos 2x = \cos (x + x)$, we apply (2) to obtain:

(5)
$$\cos 2x = \cos^2 x - \sin^2 x$$

which by (3) can be written in any of the following forms:

(6)
$$\cos 2x = 2 \cos^2 x - 1 \qquad \cos 2x = 1 - 2 \sin^2 x$$
$$\cos^2 x = \tfrac{1}{2}(1 + \cos 2x) \qquad \sin^2 x = \tfrac{1}{2}(1 - \cos 2x)$$

If we add the two equations in (1) we obtain:

(7)
$$\sin x \cos y = \tfrac{1}{2}[\sin (x + y) + \sin (x - y)]$$

and by first adding and then subtracting the two equations in (2),

(8)
$$\cos x \cos y = \tfrac{1}{2}[\cos (x + y) + \cos (x - y)]$$
$$\sin x \sin y = \tfrac{1}{2}[\cos (x - y) - \cos (x + y)]$$

By (3), even powers of the sine can be easily written in terms of the cosine and even powers of the cosine can be written in terms of the sine:

$$\sin^4 x = (\sin^2 x)^2 = (1 - \cos^2 x)^2 = 1 - 2 \cos^2 x + \cos^4 x$$

Similarly, even powers of the secant can be written by (4) in terms of the tangent and even powers of the tangent in terms of the secant:

$$\tan^6 x = (\tan^2 x)^3 = (\sec^2 x - 1)^3 = \sec^6 x - 3 \sec^4 x + 3 \sec^2 x - 1$$

By (6), even powers of the sine and cosine can be *reduced* in terms of the cosine of the double angle

$$\sin^4 x = (\sin^2 x)^2 = [\tfrac{1}{2}(1 - \cos 2x)]^2 = \tfrac{1}{4}(1 - 2 \cos 2x + \cos^2 2x)$$

Identities (7) and (8) permit the writing of products of sines and cosines as sums. All these maneuvers will be useful in the problems that follow.

Products of Powers of Sines and Cosines–When an Odd Integral Power Appears Consider $\int \sin^m x \cos^n x \, dx$, where, say, n is an *odd* positive integer. This may be written as

$$\int \sin^m x \cos^{n-1} x \cos x \, dx$$

Since $n - 1$ is an *even* integer and $\cos^2 x = 1 - \sin^2 x$, $\cos^{n-1} x$ can be written as a polynomial in $\sin x$. If we now apply the change-of-variable technique: $u = \sin x$, $du = \cos x \, dx$, we obtain a sum of integrals of the form $\int u^k \, du$, each of which can be evaluated by recognition.

74 a $\int \sin^2 x \cos^3 x \, dx = ?$

b $\int \sqrt{\sin x} \cos^3 x \, dx = ?$

c $\int \sin^5 x \cos^4 x \, dx = ?$ [Write $\sin^5 x = \sin^4 x \sin x$, then write $\sin^4 x = (\sin^2 x)^2 = (1 - \cos^2 x)^2 = 1 - 2\cos^2 x + \cos^4 x$ and proceed.]

d $\int \sin^5 x \, dx = ?$

e In deriving $\int 65$, we let $u = \sin x$ and need, in order to change variables, the derivative $\cos x$ of this function as a factor of the integrand. When an *odd* integral power of the cosine appears in the integrand, a factor $\cos x$ is removed and the remaining *even* power of $\cos x$ can be written as a polynomial in $\sin x$. Now *try* to apply this same method to the following problem, where only even powers appear: $\int \sin^4 x \cos^2 x \, dx = ?$ Are you in trouble?

Products of Powers of Sines and Cosines–When Only Even Integral Powers Appear   Here the half-angle formulas from trigonometry,

$$\cos^2 x = \tfrac{1}{2}(1 + \cos 2x) \qquad \sin^2 x = \tfrac{1}{2}(1 - \cos 2x)$$

are useful. For example

$$
\begin{aligned}
\int \sin^2 x \, dx &= \int \tfrac{1}{2}(1 - \cos 2x) \, dx \\
&= \int \tfrac{1}{2} \, dx - \tfrac{1}{2} \int \cos 2x \, dx \\
&= \tfrac{1}{2}x - \tfrac{1}{4} \int \cos u \, du \big|^{u=2x} \\
&= \tfrac{1}{2}x - \tfrac{1}{4} \sin 2x + C \qquad \text{(see } \int 51)
\end{aligned}
$$

---

75 $\int \cos^2 x \, dx = ?$

76 $\int \sin^2 2x \, dx = ?$

74 a $$\int \sin^2 x \cos^2 x \cos x \, dx = \int \sin^2 x \, (1 - \sin^2 x) \cos x \, dx$$

$$= \int (\sin^2 x - \sin^4 x) \cos x \, dx$$

$$= \int (u^2 - u^4) \, du \Big|^{u=\sin x}$$

$$= \frac{u^3}{3} - \frac{u^5}{5} + C \Big|^{u=\sin x}$$

$$= \frac{\sin^3 x}{3} - \frac{\sin^5 x}{5} + C$$

b $\int (\sin x)^{\frac{1}{2}} \cos^2 x \cos x \, dx = \int \sin^{\frac{1}{2}} x \, (1 - \sin^2 x) \cos x \, dx$
$$= \int \sin^{\frac{1}{2}} x \cos x \, dx - \int \sin^{\frac{5}{2}} x \cos x \, dx$$
$$= \text{(by } \int 65) \; \tfrac{2}{3} \sin^{\frac{3}{2}} x - \tfrac{2}{7} \sin^{\frac{7}{2}} x + C$$

c $\int \sin^5 x \cos^4 x \, dx = \int \sin^4 x \cos^4 x \sin x \, dx$
$$= \int (1 - 2 \cos^2 x + \cos^4 x) \cos^4 x \sin x \, dx$$
$$= \int \cos^4 x \sin x \, dx - 2 \int \cos^6 x \sin x \, dx$$
$$+ \int \cos^8 x \sin x \, dx$$
$$= \text{(by } \int 64 \text{ or change of variables)}$$
$$= -\tfrac{1}{5} \cos^5 x + \tfrac{2}{7} \cos^7 x - \tfrac{1}{9} \cos^9 x + C$$

d $\sin^5 x = (\sin^2 x)^2 \sin x = (1 - \cos^2 x)^2 \sin x$
$$= (1 - 2 \cos^2 x + \cos^4 x) \sin x$$
$\int \sin^5 x \, dx = \int (1 - 2 \cos^2 x + \cos^4 x) \sin x \, dx$
$$= -\int (1 - 2u^2 + u^4) \, du \big|^{u=\cos x}$$
$$= -(u - \tfrac{2}{3} u^3 + \tfrac{1}{5} u^5) + C \big|^{u=\cos x}$$
$$= -\cos x + \tfrac{2}{3} \cos^3 x - \tfrac{1}{5} \cos^5 x + C$$

e $\sin^4 x \cos^2 x = \sin^4 x \cos x \cos x$
$$= \sin^4 x \sqrt{1 - \sin^2 x} \cos x$$
$\int \sin^4 x \cos^2 x \, dx = \int \sin^4 x \sqrt{1 - \sin^2 x} \cos x \, dx$

and the integrand does not simplify. We will next suggest a different method, applicable to even powers of the sine and cosine.

75 $\int \cos^2 x \, dx = \int \tfrac{1}{2}(1 + \cos 2x) \, dx = $ (as in remark above)
$$= \tfrac{1}{2}x + \tfrac{1}{4} \sin 2x + C \quad \text{(See } \int 54)$$

76 $\int \sin^2 2x \, dx = \tfrac{1}{2} \int \sin^2 u \, du \big|^{u=2x} = $ (by method of remark above)
$$= \tfrac{1}{4}u - \tfrac{1}{8} \sin 2u + C \big|^{u=2x} = \tfrac{1}{2}x - \tfrac{1}{8} \sin 4x + C$$

77 $\int \sin^2 x \cos^2 x \, dx = ?$

78 $\int \cos^2 2x \, dx = ?$

79 $\int \cos^4 x \, dx = ?$

80 $\int \cos^3 x \, dx = ?$

81 **a** Integration by parts is also applicable when the integrand is a positive integral power (>1) of the sine or cosine. Consider

$\int \cos^n x \, dx = \int \cos^{n-1} x \cos x \, dx$.

Let $u = \cos^{n-1} x$ and $dv = \cos x \, dx$, and write the corresponding instance of the integration-by-parts formula.

b In Frame **81a**, substitute $(1 - \cos^2 x)$ for $\sin^2 x$ and then solve, algebraically, the resulting equation for $\int \cos^n x \, dx$.

c Apply $\int 56$ to evaluate $\int \cos^2 x \, dx$.

77 $\int \sin^2 x \cos^2 x \, dx = \int \frac{1}{2}(1 - \cos 2x)\frac{1}{2}(1 + \cos 2x) \, dx$
$$= \frac{1}{4}\int(1 - \cos^2 2x) \, dx = \frac{1}{4}\int \sin^2 2x \, dx$$
$$= \frac{1}{8}x - \frac{1}{32} \sin 4x + C \qquad \text{(See Frame 76)}$$

78 $\int \cos^2 2x \, dx = \frac{1}{2}\int \cos^2 u \, du\big|^{u=2x}$
$$= \frac{1}{4}u + \frac{1}{8} \sin 2u + C\big|^{u=2x} \qquad \text{(See Frame 75)}$$
$$= \frac{1}{2}x + \frac{1}{8} \sin 4x + C$$

79 $\int \cos^4 x \, dx = \int (\cos^2 x)^2 \, dx = \int \frac{1}{4}(1 + \cos 2x)^2 \, dx$
$$= \int \frac{1}{4} \, dx + \frac{1}{2}\int \cos 2x \, dx + \frac{1}{4}\int \cos^2 2x \, dx$$
$$= \frac{1}{4}x + \frac{1}{4} \sin 2x + \frac{1}{8}x + \frac{1}{32} \sin 4x + C \qquad \text{(See Frame 78)}$$
$$= \frac{3}{8}x + \frac{1}{4} \sin 2x + \frac{1}{32} \sin 4x + C$$

80 This is an odd power of the cosine; the half-angle formula method will not work.

$\int \cos^3 x \, dx = \int \cos^2 x \cos x \, dx = \int(1 - \sin^2 x) \cos x \, dx$
$$= \int(1 - u^2) \, du\big|^{u=\sin x}$$
$$= \sin x - \frac{1}{3} \sin^3 x + C \qquad \text{(Compare with } \int 55)$$

81 a $\begin{cases} u = \cos^{n-1} x \\ dv = \cos x \, dx \end{cases} \quad \begin{cases} du = -(n-1) \cos^{n-2} x \sin x \, dx \\ v = \sin x \end{cases}$

$\int \cos^{n-1} x \cos x \, dx = \sin x \cos^{n-1} x + (n-1)\int \cos^{n-2} x \sin^2 x \, dx.$

b $1 \cdot \int \cos^n x \, dx = \sin x \cos^{n-1} x + (n-1)\int \cos^{n-2} x \, dx$
$$- (n-1)\int \cos^n x \, dx$$
$n\int \cos^n x \, dx = \sin x \cos^{n-1} x + (n-1)\int \cos^{n-2} x \, dx$
$$\int \cos^n x \, dx = \frac{1}{n} \sin x \cos^{n-1} x + \frac{n-1}{n} \int \cos^{n-2} x \, dx$$

(See $\int 56$ and, correspondingly, $\int 53$. These are also called *reduction formulas;* note that the powers of the sines and cosines are reduced by 2.)

c Replace n by 2.
$\int \cos^2 x \, dx = \frac{1}{2} \sin x \cos x + \frac{1}{2}\int dx$
$$= \frac{1}{2} \sin x \cos x + \frac{1}{2}x + C \qquad \text{(See } \int 54)$$

d   Apply ∫53 to evaluate $\int \sin^3 x \, dx$.

e   Apply ∫53 and ∫52 to evaluate $\int \sin^5 x \, dx$.

Products of Powers of Tangents and Secants—When an Even Integral Power of the Secant Appears   This method is dependent on

(1) $$\int \tan^m x \sec^2 x \, dx = \frac{\tan^{m+1} x}{m+1} + C \qquad (m \neq -1)$$

Here the integral is of the form $\int u^m \, du$, where $u = \tan x$ and thus $du = \sec^2 x \, dx$. The trigonometric identity $\sec^2 x = 1 + \tan^2 x$ permits the writing of an even power of the secant as a polynomial in $\tan x$. If, for example, $\sec^6 x$ appears as a factor of such an integrand we can write

$$\begin{aligned}
\sec^6 x &= (\sec^2 x)^2 \sec^2 x = (1 + \tan^2 x)^2 \sec^2 x \\
&= (1 + 2\tan^2 x + \tan^4 x) \sec^2 x \\
&= \sec^2 x + 2\tan^2 x \sec^2 x + \tan^4 x \sec^2 x
\end{aligned}$$

each term of which is in the form of the integrand of (1).

82 $\int \sec^4 x \, dx = ?$

83 $\int \tan^3 x \sec^4 x \, dx = ?$

84 $\int \sqrt{\tan x} \sec^6 x \, dx = ?$

85   Corresponding methods are applicable to products of the cotangent and cosecant (when an even power of the cosecant appears).   Here we have

$$\csc^2 x = 1 + \cot^2 x \qquad \text{and} \qquad D_x \cot x = -\csc^2 x.$$

Thus

$$\int \cot^m x \csc^2 x \, dx = -\frac{\cot^{m+1} x}{m+1} + C.$$

Apply this method to evaluate $\int \cot^3 x \csc^4 x \, dx$.

d Replace n by 3.

$$\int \sin^3 x \, dx = -\tfrac{1}{3} \sin^2 x \cos x + \tfrac{2}{3}\int \sin x \, dx$$
$$= -\tfrac{1}{3} \sin^2 x \cos x - \tfrac{2}{3} \cos x + C$$
$$= -\tfrac{1}{3} \cos x \, (\sin^2 x + 2) + C \qquad (\text{See } \int 52)$$

e

$$\int \sin^5 x \, dx = -\frac{\sin^4 x \cos x}{5} + \frac{4}{5} \int \sin^3 x \, dx$$
$$= -\frac{\sin^4 x \cos x}{5} + \tfrac{4}{5}[-\tfrac{1}{3} \cos x \, (\sin^2 x + 2)] + C$$

82 $\int \sec^4 x \, dx = \int \sec^2 x \sec^2 x \, dx = \int (1 + \tan^2 x) \sec^2 x \, dx$
$\qquad\qquad = \int \sec^2 x \, dx + \int \tan^2 x \sec^2 x \, dx$
$\qquad\qquad = \tan x + \tfrac{1}{3} \tan^3 x + C$

Evaluate $\int \tan^2 x \sec^2 x \, dx$ by change of variable: $u = \tan x$, $du = \sec^2 x \, dx$.

83 Write $\sec^4 x = \sec^2 x \sec^2 x = (1 + \tan^2 x) \sec^2 x$. Thus,

$\int \tan^3 x \sec^4 x \, dx = \int \tan^3 x (1 + \tan^2 x) \sec^2 x \, dx$
$\qquad\qquad = \int \tan^3 x \sec^2 x \, dx + \int \tan^5 x \sec^2 x \, dx$
$\qquad\qquad = \tfrac{1}{4} \tan^4 x + \tfrac{1}{6} \tan^6 x + C.$

84 $\sec^6 x = \sec^4 x \sec^2 x = (1 + \tan^2 x)^2 \sec^2 x$
$\qquad\quad = (1 + 2 \tan^2 x + \tan^4 x) \sec^2 x$

$\int \sqrt{\tan x} \sec^6 x \, dx = \int \tan^{\frac{1}{2}} x \, (1 + 2 \tan^2 x + \tan^4 x) \sec^2 x \, dx$
$\qquad\qquad = \int \tan^{\frac{1}{2}} x \sec^2 x \, dx + 2 \int \tan^{\frac{5}{2}} x \sec^2 x \, dx$
$\qquad\qquad\qquad\qquad\qquad + \int \tan^{\frac{9}{2}} x \sec^2 x \, dx$
$\qquad\qquad = \tfrac{2}{3} \tan^{\frac{3}{2}} x + \tfrac{4}{7} \tan^{\frac{7}{2}} x + \tfrac{2}{11} \tan^{\frac{11}{2}} x + C$

85 $\csc^4 x = \csc^2 x \csc^2 x = (1 + \cot^2 x) \csc^2 x$

$\int \cot^3 x \csc^4 x \, dx = \int \cot^3 x \, (1 + \cot^2 x) \csc^2 x \, dx$
$\qquad\qquad = \int \cot^3 x \csc^2 x \, dx + \int \cot^5 x \csc^2 x \, dx$
$\qquad\qquad = -\tfrac{1}{4} \cot^4 x - \tfrac{1}{6} \cot^6 x + C$

Products of Powers of Tangents and Secants–When an Odd Integral Power of the Tangent Appears   We here consider integrals of the form $\int \tan^m x \sec^n x \, dx$ where m is an *odd* positive integer.   If n is an even positive integer, previous methods apply.   The trickery here is to write the integral as a sum of integrals in the form $\int \sec^a x \sec x \tan x \, dx$ so that the change in variable $u = \sec x$, thus $du = \sec x \tan x \, dx$, permits us to write this last integral in the easily handled form $\int u^a \, du |^{u=\sec x}$.   To prepare for this change in variables we need $\sec x \tan x \, dx$ as a factor.   Thus we write

$$\int \tan^m x \sec^n x \, dx = \int \tan^{m-1} x \sec^{n-1} x \sec x \tan x \, dx$$

Since m is odd, $m - 1$ is even and $\tan^{m-1} x$ can be written as a polynomial in $(\sec x)$ via the trigonometric identity $\tan^2 x = \sec^2 x - 1$.

86 $\int \sec^3 x \tan x \, dx = ?$

87 $\int \sec^3 x \tan^3 x \, dx = ?$ Note that an odd power of the tangent appears.

88 $\int \sec^{\frac{1}{2}} x \tan x \, dx = ?$

89 $\int \sqrt{\sec x} \tan^3 x \, dx = ?$

90 $\int \tan^3 x \, dx = ?$ $\left(\text{Note:} \dfrac{1}{\sec x} \sec x = 1 \right)$

Positive Integral Powers of the Secant   Integrands consisting of even positive integral powers of the secant are best handled by the methods above.   Odd powers are best handled by the reduction formula $\int 59$ which we will derive in Frame **91a** to **e**.   We need apply the previously derived formula $\int 49$ and the trigonometric identities

$$\tan^2 x = \sec^2 x - 1 \qquad \sec x = \frac{1}{\cos x}$$

86 $\int \sec^3 x \tan x \, dx = \int \sec^2 x \sec x \tan x \, dx = \int u^2 \, du \big|^{u=\sec x}$
$$= \tfrac{1}{3} u^3 + C \big|^{u=\sec x} = \tfrac{1}{3} \sec^3 x + C$$

87 $\int \sec^3 x \tan^3 x \, dx = \int \sec^2 x \tan^2 x \sec x \tan x \, dx$
$$= \int \sec^2 x \, (\sec^2 x - 1) \sec x \tan x \, dx$$
$$= \int u^2(u^2 - 1) \, du \big|^{u=\sec x} = \int (u^4 - u^2) \, du \big|^{u=\sec x}$$
$$= \tfrac{1}{5} u^5 - \tfrac{1}{3} u^3 + C \big|^{u=\sec x} = \tfrac{1}{5} \sec^5 x - \tfrac{1}{3} \sec^3 x + C$$

88 $\int \sec^{\frac{1}{2}} x \tan x \, dx = \int \sec^{-\frac{1}{2}} x \sec x \tan x \, dx = \int u^{\frac{1}{2}} \, du \big|^{u=\sec x}$
$$= \tfrac{2}{3} u^{\frac{3}{2}} + C \big|^{u=\sec x} = \tfrac{2}{3} \sec^{\frac{3}{2}} x + C$$

89 $\int \sec^{\frac{1}{2}} x \tan^3 x \, dx = \int \sec^{-\frac{1}{2}} x \tan^2 x \sec x \tan x \, dx$
$$= \int \sec^{-\frac{1}{2}} x (\sec^2 x - 1) \sec x \tan x \, dx$$
$$= \int u^{-\frac{1}{2}}(u^2 - 1) \, du \big|^{u=\sec x}$$
$$= \int (u^{\frac{3}{2}} - u^{-\frac{1}{2}}) \, du \big|^{u=\sec x} = \tfrac{2}{5} u^{\frac{5}{2}} - 2u^{\frac{1}{2}} + C \big|^{u=\sec x}$$
$$= \tfrac{2}{5} \sec^{\frac{5}{2}} x - 2 \sec^{\frac{1}{2}} x + C$$

90 $\displaystyle \int \tan^3 x \, dx = \int \frac{1}{\sec x} \tan^2 x \sec x \tan x \, dx$

$$= \int \frac{1}{\sec x} (\sec^2 x - 1) \sec x \tan x \, dx$$

$$= \int \frac{1}{u} (u^2 - 1) \, du \bigg|^{u=\sec x} = \int \left(u - \frac{1}{u} \right) du \bigg|^{u=\sec x}$$

$$= \tfrac{1}{2} u^2 - \ln u + C \big|^{u=\sec x} = \tfrac{1}{2} \sec^2 x - \ln \sec x + C$$

91 **a** Write $\int \sec^n x \, dx = \int \sec^{n-2} x \sec^2 x \, dx$, let $u = \sec^{n-2} x$, $dv = \sec^2 x \, dx$, and write the corresponding instance of the integration-by-parts formula.

    b In Frame **91a**, replace $\tan^2 x$ by $\sec^2 x - 1$, then solve the resulting equation algebraically for $\int \sec^n x \, dx$.

    c Apply $\int 59$ and $\int 49$ to evaluate $\int \sec^3 x \, dx$.

    d Apply Frame **91c** to evaluate $\int \sec^3 5x \, dx$.

    e The formula $\int 59$ is applicable also to even powers of the secant, and corresponding formulas can be derived to handle positive powers of the cosecant. Apply $\int 59$ to evaluate $\int (\sec x)^4 \, dx$.

Positive Integral Powers of the Tangent   The first power of the tangent is integrable as follows:

$$\int \tan x \, dx = \int \frac{\sin x}{\cos x} \, dx$$
$$= -\int \frac{1}{u} \, du \Big|^{u=\cos x}$$
$$= -\ln u + C \big|^{u=\cos x}$$
$$= -\ln \cos x + C \qquad (\text{see } \int 47)$$

If $n > 1$, the reduction formula $\int 68$, which we derive in the following exercises, is applicable. This is a reduction formula which does not result from an application of integration by parts.

---

92 Evaluate $\int \tan^2 x \, dx$ by writing the integrand in terms of the secant function.

93 Evaluate $\int \cot^2 x \, dx$.

94 Write

$$\int \tan^3 x \, dx = \int \tan x \tan^2 x \, dx = \int \tan x (\sec^2 x - 1) \, dx$$

and evaluate.

91 a $\begin{cases} u = \sec^{n-2} x \\ dv = \sec^2 x \, dx \end{cases} \quad \begin{cases} du = (n-2) \sec^{n-3} x \sec x \tan x \, dx \\ v = \tan x \end{cases}$

$\int \sec^n x \, dx = \sec^{n-2} x \tan x - (n-2) \int \sec^{n-2} x \tan^2 x \, dx$

b $\qquad \int \sec^n x \, dx = \sec^{n-2} x \tan x - (n-2) \int \sec^n x \, dx$

$$+ (n-2) \int \sec^{n-2} x \, dx$$

$$(n-1) \int \sec^n x \, dx = \sec^{n-2} x \tan x + (n-2) \int \sec^{n-2} x \, dx$$

$$\int \sec^n x \, dx = \frac{\sec^{n-2} x \tan x}{n-1} + \frac{n-2}{n-1} \int \sec^{n-2} x \, dx$$

(Compare this with $\int 59$.)

c Replace n by 3.

$\int \sec^3 x \, dx = \frac{1}{2} \sec x \tan x + \frac{1}{2} \int \sec x \, dx$
$\qquad\qquad = \frac{1}{2} \sec x \tan x + \frac{1}{2} \ln (\sec x + \tan x) + C$

d $\int \sec^3 5x \, dx = \frac{1}{5} \int \sec^3 u \, du \,|^{u=5x}$
$\qquad\qquad = \frac{1}{10} \sec u \tan u + \frac{1}{10} \ln (\sec u + \tan u) + C \,|^{u=5x}$
$\qquad\qquad = \frac{1}{10} \sec 5x \tan 5x + \frac{1}{10} \ln (\sec 5x + \tan 5x) + C$

e Replace n by 4.

$\int \sec^4 x \, dx = \frac{1}{3} \sec^2 x \tan x + \frac{2}{3} \int \sec^2 x \, dx$
$\qquad\qquad = \frac{1}{3} \sec^2 x \tan x + \frac{2}{3} \tan x + C$

92 $\int \tan^2 x \, dx = \int (\sec^2 x - 1) \, dx = \tan x - x + C$ (See $\int 67$)

93 $\int \cot^2 x \, dx = \int (\csc^2 x - 1) \, dx = -\cot x - x + C$ (See $\int 69$)

94 $\displaystyle\int \tan^3 x \, dx = \int \tan x \, (\sec^2 x - 1) \, dx$

$$= \int \tan x \sec^2 x \, dx - \int \frac{\sin x}{\cos x} \, dx$$

$$= \int u \, du \, \Big|^{u=\tan x} + \int \frac{1}{v} \, dv \, \Big|^{v=\cos x}$$

$$= \frac{1}{2} u^2 \,|^{u=\tan x} + \ln v \,|^{v=\cos x} + C$$

$$= \frac{1}{2} \tan^2 x + \ln (\cos x) + C$$

95 If $n \geq 2$, write

$$\tan^n x = \tan^{n-2} x \tan^2 x = \tan^{n-2} x(\sec^2 x - 1)$$

and derive $\int 68$.

96 Apply $\int 68$ to evaluate $\int \tan^2 x \, dx$.

97 Apply $\int 68$ to evaluate $\int \tan^3 x \, dx$.

98 **a** Write $\tan^4 x \sec^3 x$ as a polynomial in $\sec x$.

 b Explain (but do not evaluate) how you would evaluate $\int \tan^4 x \sec^3 x \, dx$.

 c Explain how you could evaluate $\int \tan^m x \sec^n x \, dx$ if m is a positive *even* integer, n a positive integer.

Products of Sines and Cosines   The student should verify the following identities which write products of sines and cosines as sums:

$$\sin x \cos y = \tfrac{1}{2} \sin (x + y) + \tfrac{1}{2} \sin (x - y)$$
$$\cos x \cos y = \tfrac{1}{2} \cos (x + y) + \tfrac{1}{2} \cos (x - y)$$
$$\sin x \sin y = \tfrac{1}{2} \cos (x - y) - \tfrac{1}{2} \cos (x + y)$$

These identities lead immediately to integration formulas $\int 60$, $\int 61$, $\int 63$. In Frames **99** to **101**, we apply the identities to derive a few instances of the tabulated integration formulas.

99 **a** $\int \sin 4x \cos 3x \, dx = ?$ Apply one of the identities of the remark above.

 b Evaluate $\int \sin 4x \cos 3x \, dx$ as an instance of $\int 63$.

100 **a** $\int \sin 4x \sin 3x \, dx = ?$ Apply one of the identities above.

 b Evaluate $\int \sin 4x \sin 3x \, dx$ as an instance of $\int 60$.

95 $\displaystyle\int \tan^n x\, dx = \int \tan^{n-2} x \sec^2 x\, dx - \int \tan^{n-2} x\, dx$

$$= \int u^{n-2}\, du \Big|^{u=\tan x} - \int \tan^{n-2} x\, dx$$

$$= \frac{u^{n-1}}{n-1}\Big|^{u=\tan x} - \int \tan^{n-2} x\, dx$$

$$= \frac{\tan^{n-1} x}{n-1} - \int \tan^{n-2} x\, dx$$

$\int$70 is similarly derived.

96 Replace n by 2.
$\int \tan^2 x\, dx = \tan x - \int 1\, dx = \tan x - x + C$

97 Replace n by 3.
$\int \tan^3 x\, dx = \frac{1}{2}\tan^2 x - \int \tan x\, dx = \frac{1}{2}\tan^2 x + \ln(\cos x) + C$

98 **a** $\tan^4 x \sec^3 x = (\tan^2 x)^2 \sec^3 x = (\sec^2 x - 1)^2 \sec^3 x$
$$= (\sec^4 x - 2\sec^2 x + 1)\sec^3 x$$
$$= \sec^7 x - 2\sec^5 x + \sec^3 x$$

    b $\tan^4 x \sec^3 x$ can be written as a sum of powers of the secant (see Frame **98a**), and each such power can be integrated by repeated application of $\int$59.

    c $\tan^m x \sec^n x$ can be written, via $\tan^2 x = \sec^2 x - 1$, as a polynomial in $\sec x$, each term of which is integrable by repeated applications of $\int$59.

99 **a** $\int \sin 4x \cos 3x\, dx = \frac{1}{2}\int (\sin 7x + \sin x)\, dx$
$$= -\tfrac{1}{14}\cos 7x - \tfrac{1}{2}\cos x + C$$

    b   Replace m by 4 and n by 3.
$$\int \sin 4x \cos 3x\, dx = -\frac{\cos x}{2} - \frac{\cos 7x}{14} + C$$

100 **a** $\int \sin 4x \sin 3x\, dx = \frac{1}{2}\int (\cos x - \cos 7x)\, dx$
$$= \tfrac{1}{2}\sin x - \tfrac{1}{14}\sin 7x + C$$

    b   Replace m by 4 and n by 3.
$$\int \sin 4x \sin 3x\, dx = \frac{\sin x}{2} - \frac{\sin 7x}{14} + C$$

101 **a** $\int \cos 4x \cos 3x \, dx = $?   Apply one of the identities in the remark above.

b Evaluate $\int \cos 4x \cos 3x \, dx$ as an instance of $\int 61$.

On Inverse Functions If g and h are two functions defined on suitable domains, then we say that h *is the inverse* of g if and only if their composition $g[h(x)]$ is the identity function on the domain of h, i.e., $g[h(x)] = x$. This can also be written in the composite form $g(t)\big|^{t=h(x)} = x$.

---

102 Let $g(t) = t^2$ and $h(x) = \sqrt{x}$.   Show that h is the inverse of g.   On what largest domain is this true?

103 Let $g(t) = t^3$ and $h(x) = \sqrt[3]{x}$.   Show that h is the inverse of g.   On what largest domain?

104 Let $g(t) = \sin t$ and $h(x) = \arcsin x$.   Show that h is the inverse of g. On what largest domain?

105 Let $g(t) = \tan t$ and $h(x) = \arctan x$.   Show that h is the inverse of g.   On what largest domain?

106 If $g(t) = e^t$ and $h(x) = \ln x$, show that h is the inverse of g.   On what largest domain?

107 If $g(t) = \ln t$ and $h(x) = e^x$, show that h is the inverse of g.   On what largest domain?

108 If $g(t) = t - 1$, find a function $h(x)$ which is the inverse of g.   Do this by writing $x = g(t) = t - 1$ and solve for t as a function of x.

109 If $g(t) = t^3$, find a function $h(x)$ which is the inverse of g.

110 If $g(t) = \sin t$, find a function $h(x)$ which is the inverse of g.

111 If $g(t) = (t - 1)^2$, find a function $h(x)$ which is the inverse of g. (Assume $x \geq 0$.)

101 **a** $\int \cos 4x \cos 3x\,dx = \frac{1}{2}\int (\cos 7x + \cos x)\,dx$
$$= \frac{1}{14}\sin 7x + \frac{1}{2}\sin x + C$$

b Replace m by 4 and n by 3.
$$\int \cos 4x \cos 3x\,dx = \frac{\sin x}{2} + \frac{\sin 7x}{14} + C$$

102 $g(t)\big|_{t=h(x)} = t^2\big|_{t=\sqrt{x}} = (\sqrt{x})^2 = x$, true for all $x \geq 0$.

103 $g(t)\big|_{t=h(x)} = t^3\big|_{t=\sqrt[3]{x}} = (\sqrt[3]{x})^3 = x$, for all x.

104 $g(t)\big|_{t=h(x)} = \sin t\big|_{t=\arcsin x}$
$$= \sin(\arcsin x) = x, \text{ if } -1 \leq x \leq 1.$$

105 $g(t)\big|_{t=h(x)} = \tan t\big|_{t=\arctan x} = \tan(\arctan x) = x$, for all x.

106 $g(t)\big|_{t=h(x)} = e^t\big|_{t=\ln x} = e^{\ln x} = x$, if $x > 0$.

107 $g(t)\big|_{t=h(x)} = \ln t\big|_{t=e^x} = \ln(e^x) = x \ln e = x$, for all x.

108 $x = t - 1 \qquad t = x + 1 = h(x)$
To check, note
$$g(t)\big|_{t=h(x)} = t - 1\big|_{t=x+1} = (x+1) - 1 = x.$$

109 Write $x = t^3$; solve for t: $t = \sqrt[3]{x} = h(x)$. Check:
$$g(t)\big|_{t=h(x)} = t^3\big|_{t=\sqrt[3]{x}} = (\sqrt[3]{x})^3 = x.$$

110 Write $x = \sin t$; solve for t: $t = \arcsin x = h(x)$. Check:
$$g(t)\big|_{t=h(x)} = \sin t\big|_{t=\arcsin x} = \sin(\arcsin x) = x.$$

111 Write $x = (t-1)^2$; $\sqrt{x} = t - 1$; $t = 1 + \sqrt{x} = h(x)$. Check:
$$g(t)\big|_{t=h(x)} = (t-1)^2\big|_{t=1+\sqrt{x}} = [(1 + \sqrt{x}) - 1]^2 = x.$$

112 If $g(t) = t^2 - 4$, find a function $h(x)$ which is the inverse of g. (Assume $x \geq -4$.)

113 If $g(t) = \frac{1}{3}(t^3 + 1)$, find a function $h(x)$ which is the inverse of g.

Second Change-of-variable Procedure An important theorem about inverse functions states that if the function g has a derivative g' and if h is the inverse of g, then h will have a derivative h'. In this case, since $g(t)|^{t=h(x)} = x$, $D_x g(t)|^{t=h(x)} = D_x x = 1$, and applying the chain rule to this we obtain

(1) $$g'(t) \cdot h'(x)|^{t=h(x)} = 1$$

A very useful change-of-variable procedure for integration is based on the following theorem:

(2) $$\int f(x)\,dx = \int f[g(t)] \cdot g'(t)\,dt|^{t=h(x)}$$

where h is the inverse of g, a proof of which we now indicate.

Let $F(t)$ be an antiderivative of $f[g(t)]g'(t)$, i.e., $D_t F(t) = f[g(t)]g'(t)$. Then, by the chain rule,

$$D_x F(t)|^{t=h(x)} = f[g(t)] \cdot g'(t) \cdot h'(x)|^{t=h(x)}$$

The first factor on the right is $f\{g[h(x)]\}$, which, since h is the inverse function of g, equals $f(x)$. The remaining factor $g'(t) \cdot h'(x)|^{t=h(x)} = 1$ by (1). Thus $D_x F(t)|^{t=h(x)} = f(x)$, and $F[h(x)]$ is an antiderivative of $f(x)$. In application, if we are able to find an antiderivative of $f[g(t)] \cdot g'(t)$, then (2) exhibits an antiderivative of $f(x)$. Though the integral on the right looks more complicated than the one on the left, this may not in fact be so in particular cases after simplification.

Look now at formula (2) in an operational sense:

1 Consider $\int f(x)\,dx$, which we assume we cannot evaluate by inspection or by the methods already introduced.
2 If the structure of the integrand in $\int f(x)\,dx$ suggests replacing x by some function $g(t)$ and if we so replace x by $g(t)$ and at the same time replace dx by $g'(t)\,dt$, we obtain $\int f[g(t)] \cdot g'(t)\,dt$, the integral on the right of (2).
3 If we can find a function $F(t)$ such that

$$\int f[g(t)] \cdot g'(t)\,dt = F(t) + C$$

112 Write $x = t^2 - 4$; $t^2 = x + 4$; $t = \sqrt{x+4} = h(x)$. Check:

$g(t)\big|_{t=h(x)} = t^2 - 4\big|_{t=\sqrt{x+4}} = (\sqrt{x+4})^2 - 4 = x + 4 - 4 = x.$

113 Write $x = \frac{1}{3}(t^3 + 1)$; $3x - 1 = t^3$; $t = \sqrt[3]{3x-1} = h(x)$. Check:

$g(t)\big|_{t=h(x)} = \frac{1}{3}(t^3 + 1)\big|_{t=\sqrt[3]{3x-1}} = \frac{1}{3}[(3x - 1) + 1] = x.$

then we have

$$\int f(x)\, dx = F(t) + C\big|^{t=h(x)}$$

where h is the inverse function of g. We *do not* apply this procedure unless such a function h exists.

Integration, in general, involves trial-and-error procedures. We try this second change-of-variable procedure when the structure of the integrand of $\int f(x)\, dx$ suggests that the resulting integral $\int f[g(t)] \cdot g'(t)\, dt$ will be more amenable than the original integral. If this does not result, we must be prepared to abandon the attempt and try something else.

---

114 a Consider $\displaystyle\int \frac{1}{1 + \sqrt{x}}\, dx$ and note the troublesome denominator $1 + \sqrt{x}$. By what function $g(t)$ would you replace x, so that the denominator becomes simply the expression t?

b In the integral of Frame **114a**, replace x by $(t - 1)^2$. If we are to apply the second change-of-variable procedure, by what will you replace dx? Find also a function which is the inverse of $(t - 1)^2$. Call it $h(x)$.

c Apply Frame **114a** and **b** to evaluate $\displaystyle\int \frac{1}{1 + \sqrt{x}}\, dx$.

115 a Consider $\int x \sqrt[3]{x + 1}\, dx$ and note the troublesome factor $\sqrt[3]{x + 1}$. By what function $g(t)$ would you replace x so that this factor becomes simply t?

b Show that $h(x) = \sqrt[3]{x + 1}$ is the inverse function to $t^3 - 1$, and evaluate $\int x \sqrt[3]{x + 1}\, dx$ by the second change-of-variable procedure.

114   **a**   Let $1 + \sqrt{x} = t$.   Then $\sqrt{x} = t - 1$, $x = (t - 1)^2 = g(t)$.

b   Replace dx by $2(t - 1)\, dt$.   If $x = (t - 1)^2$, then $\sqrt{x} = t - 1$,
$t = 1 + \sqrt{x} = h(x)$.

c $\displaystyle \int \frac{1}{1 + \sqrt{x}}\, dx = \int \frac{1}{1 + \sqrt{(t - 1)^2}}\, 2(t-1)\, dt \Big|^{t=1+\sqrt{x}}$

$\displaystyle \qquad = 2 \int \frac{t - 1}{t}\, dt$

$\displaystyle \qquad = 2 \int \left(1 - \frac{1}{t}\right) dt = 2t - 2 \ln t \Big|^{t=1+\sqrt{x}}$

$\displaystyle \qquad = 2 + 2\sqrt{x} - 2 \ln (1 + \sqrt{x}) + C$

$\displaystyle \qquad = 2\sqrt{x} - 2 \ln (1 + \sqrt{x}) + C_1$

115   **a** $t = \sqrt[3]{x + 1}$, $t^3 = x + 1$, $x = t^3 - 1 = g(t)$

b $\int x \sqrt[3]{x + 1}\, dx = \int (t^3 - 1)t\, 3\, t^2\, dt \big|^{t = \sqrt[3]{x+1}} = 3\int (t^6 - t^3)\, dt$

$\displaystyle \qquad = \tfrac{3}{7} t^7 - \tfrac{3}{4} t^4 + C \big|^{t=\sqrt[3]{x+1}}$

$\displaystyle \qquad = \tfrac{3}{7}(x + 1)^{\frac{7}{3}} - \tfrac{3}{4}(x + 1)^{\frac{4}{3}} + C$

116 **a** Consider $\displaystyle\int \frac{x}{\sqrt{x+1}}\, dx$. What part of the integrand looks troublesome?

b By what function $g(t)$ would you replace x in Frame **116a** in order to simplify the troublesome denominator?

c Change variables by setting $x = t^2 - 1$ and evaluate

$$\int \frac{x}{\sqrt{x+1}}\, dx.$$

Trigonometric Substitutions The structure of certain algebraic integrands suggests the introduction of certain trigonometric functions because they may simplify the integrands. These substitutions are based on the following trigonometric identities:

$$1 - \sin^2 t = \cos^2 t \quad \text{thus} \quad a^2 - a^2 \sin^2 t = a^2 \cos^2 t$$
$$\sec^2 t - 1 = \tan^2 t \quad \text{thus} \quad a^2 \sec^2 t - a^2 = a^2 \tan^2 t$$
$$1 + \tan^2 t = \sec^2 t \quad \text{thus} \quad a^2 + a^2 \tan^2 t = a^2 \sec^2 t$$

1   If the integrand contains the expression $a^2 - x^2$, by substituting $x = a \sin t$, we obtain $a^2 - x^2 = a^2 - a^2 \sin^2 t$, which simplifies to $a^2 \cos^2 t$.
2   If the integrand contains the expression $x^2 - a^2$, by substituting $x = a \sec t$, we obtain $x^2 - a^2 = a^2 \sec^2 t - a^2$, which simplifies to $a^2 \tan^2 t$.
3   If the integrand contains the expression $a^2 + x^2$, by substituting $x = a \tan t$, we obtain $a^2 + x^2 = a^2 + a^2 \tan^2 t = a^2 \sec^2 t$.

Our earlier preoccupation with trigonometric integrals should help us here; the student may use any tabulated formula previously derived.

---

117 $\displaystyle\int \frac{dx}{\sqrt{a^2 - x^2}} = ?$ The troublesome part of this integrand is $\sqrt{a^2 - x^2}$, and the discussion in the above remark suggests letting $x = a \sin t$. Then we must replace dx by $a \cos t\, dt$ and the inverse function is $t = \arcsin \dfrac{x}{a}$.   Evaluate the integral.

116 **a** The denominator $\sqrt{x+1}$.

    b There is no unique answer here. If we desire the denominator $\sqrt{x+1}$ to simplify to t, let $\sqrt{x+1} = t$, $x + 1 = t^2$, $x = t^2 - 1 = g(t)$.

    c $dx = 2t\,dt$ and the inverse function is given by $t = \sqrt{x+1}$.

$$\int \frac{x}{\sqrt{x+1}}\,dx = \int \frac{t^2-1}{t}\,2t\,dt \Big|^{t=\sqrt{x+1}}$$

$$= 2\int(t^2-1)\,dt = \tfrac{2}{3}t^3 - 2t + C\big|^{t=\sqrt{x+1}}$$

$$= \tfrac{2}{3}(x+1)^{\frac{3}{2}} - 2(x+1)^{\frac{1}{2}} + C$$

117 $$\int \frac{dx}{\sqrt{a^2-x^2}} = \int \frac{a\cos t}{\sqrt{a^2\cos^2 t}}\,dt \Big|^{t=\arcsin\,(x/a)}$$

$$= \int 1\,dt = t + C \Big|^{t=\arcsin\,(x/a)}$$

$$= \arcsin \frac{x}{a} + C \qquad \text{(See } \int 36)$$

118 **a** Consider $\int (a^2 - x^2)^{-\frac{3}{2}} \, dx$. Note the troublesome $(a^2 - x^2)^{-\frac{3}{2}}$. What change in variable would you make here?

b $\int (a^2 - x^2)^{-\frac{3}{2}} \, dx = ?$

c From trigonometry, if $t = \arcsin \dfrac{x}{a}$, then the six trigonometric functions of t are given by formulas consistent with those obtained from the following right triangle:

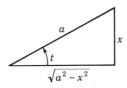

Note that the $\sin t = \dfrac{x}{a}$ and the remaining side is obtainable from the Pythagorean theorem. In particular,

$$\tan \arcsin \frac{x}{a} = \tan t = \frac{x}{\sqrt{a^2 - x^2}}$$

Substitute this in Frame **118b** and check with ∫41.

d Apply ∫41 to evaluate $\int (4 - x^2)^{-\frac{3}{2}} \, dx$.

e Apply ∫41 to evaluate $\int (3 - x^2)^{-\frac{3}{2}} \, dx$.

118 a Let $x = a \sin t$.

b Let $x = a \sin t$, then $dx = a \cos t\, dt$ and the inverse function is given by $t = \arcsin (x/a)$.

$$\int (a^2 - x^2)^{-\frac{3}{2}}\, dx = \int (a^2 \cos^2 t)^{-\frac{3}{2}} a \cos t\, dt \Big|^{t=\arcsin\ (x/a)}$$

$$= \int a^{-3} \cos^{-3} t\, a \cos t\, dt$$

$$= \frac{1}{a^2} \int \sec^2 t\, dt$$

$$= \frac{1}{a^2} \tan t + C \big|^{t=\arcsin\ (x/a)}$$

$$= \frac{1}{a^2} \tan \left(\arcsin \frac{x}{a} \right) + C$$

c $\displaystyle \int (a^2 - x^2)^{-\frac{3}{2}}\, dx = \frac{1}{a^2} \frac{x}{\sqrt{a^2 - x^2}} + C$

d Replace a by 2. $\displaystyle \int (4 - x^2)^{-\frac{3}{2}}\, dx = \frac{1}{4} \frac{x}{\sqrt{4 - x^2}} + C$

e Replace a by $\sqrt{3}$. $\displaystyle \int = \frac{1}{3} \frac{x}{\sqrt{3 - x^2}} + C$

119 **a** $\displaystyle\int \frac{dx}{x\sqrt{a^2-x^2}} = ?$

  b By rationalizing the numerator, show that $\dfrac{a-\sqrt{a^2-x^2}}{x}$ equals

  $\dfrac{x}{a+\sqrt{a^2-x^2}}$, then compare the answer to Frame **119a** with $\int 37$.

119　**a**　Let $x = a \sin t$; then $dx = a \cos t \, dt$ and the inverse function is given by $t = \arcsin (x/a)$.

$$\int = \int \frac{a \cos t \, dt}{a \sin t \sqrt{a^2 \cos^2 t}} \bigg|^{t=\arcsin \,(x/a)}$$

$$= \frac{1}{a} \int \csc t \, dt$$

$$= \frac{1}{a} \ln (\csc t - \cot t) + C \big|^{t=\arcsin \,(x/a)} \qquad \text{(by } \int 50)$$

Thus, from the triangle

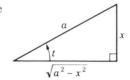

we have $\csc t = \dfrac{a}{x}$ and $\cot t = \dfrac{\sqrt{a^2 - x^2}}{x}$, hence

$$\int = \frac{1}{a} \ln \left(\frac{a - \sqrt{a^2 - x^2}}{x} \right) + C.$$

b　$\dfrac{a - \sqrt{a^2 - x^2}}{x} = \dfrac{(a - \sqrt{a^2 - x^2})(a + \sqrt{a^2 - x^2})}{x(a + \sqrt{a^2 - x^2})}$

$$= \frac{a^2 - (a^2 - x^2)}{x(a + \sqrt{a^2 - x^2})} = \frac{x}{a + \sqrt{a^2 - x^2}}$$

Also, $\ln \dfrac{1}{b} = -\ln b$.

120 $\int \sqrt{a^2 - x^2}\, dx = ?$

121 **a** Formulas $\int 39$, $\int 40$, $\int 42$, and $\int 43$, because of the factor x, lend themselves to the first change-of-variable procedure by setting $u = a^2 - x^2$; thus $du = -2x\, dx$. Evaluate $\int 39$ by this method.

    b Now apply the second change-of-variable procedure to evaluate $\int 39$.

120 Let $x = a \sin t$; then $dx = a \cos t \, dt$ and the inverse function is $t = \arcsin (x/a)$.

$$\int = \int \sqrt{a^2 \cos^2 t} \; a \cos t \, dt \Big|^{t=\arcsin \, (x/a)} = a^2 \int \cos^2 t \, dt$$

$$= \frac{a^2}{2} \sin t \cos t + \frac{a^2}{2} t + C \Big|^{t=\arcsin \, (x/a)} \qquad \text{(See } \textstyle\int 54)$$

Then from the triangle

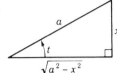

$\sin t = \dfrac{x}{a}, \cos t = \dfrac{\sqrt{a^2 - x^2}}{a}$, and we have

$$\int = \frac{a^2}{2} \frac{x}{a} \frac{\sqrt{a^2 - x^2}}{a} + \frac{a^2}{2} \arcsin \frac{x}{a} + C$$

$$= \frac{1}{2} \left(x \sqrt{a^2 - x^2} + a^2 \arcsin \frac{x}{a} \right) + C. \qquad \text{(See } \textstyle\int 35.)$$

121 **a** $\int = -\tfrac{1}{2} \int (a^2 - x^2)^{-\frac{1}{2}} (-2)x \, dx = -\tfrac{1}{2} \int u^{-\frac{1}{2}} \, du \Big|^{u=a^2-x^2}$
$\qquad = -u^{\frac{1}{2}} + C \Big|^{u=a^2-x^2} = -(a^2 - x^2)^{\frac{1}{2}} + C$

b Let $x = a \sin t$; then $dx = a \cos t \, dt$ and the inverse function is $t = \arcsin (x/a)$.

$$\int = \int \frac{a \sin t}{\sqrt{a^2 \cos^2 t}} \; a \cos t \, dt \Big|^{t=\arcsin \, (x/a)} = a \int \sin t \, dt$$

$$= -a \cos t + C \Big|^{t=\arcsin \, (x/a)}$$

From the triangle

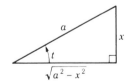

$\cos t = \dfrac{\sqrt{a^2 - x^2}}{a}$; hence $\displaystyle\int = -\sqrt{a^2 - x^2} + C.$

122 $\displaystyle\int \frac{x^2\,dx}{\sqrt{a^2 - x^2}} = ?$

123 $\displaystyle\int \frac{dx}{\sqrt{x^2 + a^2}} = ?$ Note the expression $x^2 + a^2$ in the integrand.   By the remark in item 3, following Frame **116c**, this suggests the second change-of-variable technique with $x = a \tan t$.

124 $\displaystyle\int \frac{dx}{x\,\sqrt{x^2 + a^2}} = ?$

$\int 29$, $\int 30$, $\int 32$, and $\int 33$ may all be derived by the first change-of-variable procedure, since with $u = x^2 + a^2$, $du = 2x\,dx$, and each integrand has x as a factor.

---

122 Let $x = a \sin t$, etc.

$$\int = \int \frac{a^2 \sin^2 t}{\sqrt{a^2 \cos^2 t}} a \cos t \, dt \Big|^{t=\arcsin (x/a)} = a^2 \int \sin^2 t \, dt$$

$$= -\frac{a^2}{2} \cos t \sin t + \frac{a^2}{2} t + C \Big|_{t=\arcsin (x/a)} \qquad \text{(by } \textstyle\int 51)$$

$$= -\frac{a^2}{2} \frac{\sqrt{a^2 - x^2}}{a} \frac{x}{a} + \frac{a^2}{2} \arcsin \frac{x}{a} + C$$

123 Let $x = a \tan t$; then $dx = a \sec^2 t \, dt$ and the inverse function is given by $t = \arctan (x/a)$. Note here that the six trigonometric functions of t can be read from the adjoining triangle.

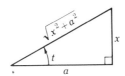

$$\int = \int \frac{a \sec^2 t}{\sqrt{a^2 \sec^2 t}} dt \Big|^{t=\arctan (x/a)} = \int \sec t \, dt$$

$$= \ln (\sec t + \tan t) + C \Big|_{t=\arctan (x/a)} \qquad \text{(by } \textstyle\int 49)$$

$$= \ln \frac{\sqrt{x^2 + a^2} + x}{a} + C$$

$$= \ln (x + \sqrt{x^2 + a^2}) - \ln a + C$$

$$= \ln (x + \sqrt{x^2 + a^2}) + C_1 \qquad \text{(See } \textstyle\int 24)$$

124 Let $x = a \tan t$; then $dx = a \sec^2 t \, dt$ and $t = \arctan (x/a)$.

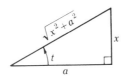

$$\int = \int \frac{a \sec^2 t \, dt}{a \tan t \sqrt{a^2 \sec^2 t}} \Big|^{t=\arctan (x/a)} = \frac{1}{a} \int \frac{\sec t}{\tan t} dt$$

$$= \frac{1}{a} \int \csc t \, dt$$

$$= \frac{1}{a} \ln (\csc t - \cot t) + C \Big|_{t=\arctan (x/a)} \qquad \text{(by } \textstyle\int 50)$$

$$= \frac{1}{a} \ln \frac{\sqrt{x^2 + a^2} - a}{x} + C \qquad \text{(This is equivalent to } \textstyle\int 26)$$

125 $\int x^3 \sqrt{x^2 + a^2}\, dx = ?$

126 $\int \sqrt{x^2 + a^2}\, dx = ?$

127 Apply $\int 24$ to evaluate $\displaystyle\int \frac{dx}{\sqrt{2x^2 + 5}}.$

125 Let $x = a \tan t$; then $dx = a \sec^2 t \, dt$, $t = \arctan (x/a)$.

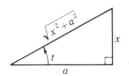

$$\int = \int a^3 \tan^3 t \sqrt{a^2 \sec^2 t} \, a \sec^2 t \, dt \Big|^{t=\arctan\ (x/a)}$$

$$= a^5 \int \tan^3 t \sec^3 t \, dt$$

$$= \frac{a^5}{5} \sec^5 t - \frac{a^5}{3} \sec^3 t + C \Big|^{t=\arctan\ (x/a)} \qquad \text{(by method of Frame 87)}$$

$$= \tfrac{1}{5}(x^2 + a^2)^{\frac{5}{2}} - \frac{a^2}{3} (x^2 + a^2)^{\frac{3}{2}} + C \qquad \text{(See } \int 34)$$

126 Let $x = a \tan t$, then $dx = a \sec^2 t \, dt$; $t = \arctan (x/a)$.

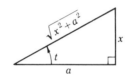

$$\int = \int \sqrt{a^2 \sec^2 t} \, a \sec^2 t \, dt \Big|^{t=\arctan\ (x/a)}$$

$$= a^2 \int \sec^3 t \, dt$$

$$= \frac{a^2}{2} \sec t \tan t + \frac{a^2}{2} \ln (\sec t + \tan t) + C \Big|^{t=\arctan\ (x/a)}$$
(Frame **91b** or $\int 59$)

$$= \frac{a^2}{2} \frac{\sqrt{x^2 + a^2}}{a} \frac{x}{a} + \frac{a^2}{2} \ln \left(\frac{\sqrt{x^2 + a^2}}{a} + \frac{x}{a} \right) + C$$

$$= \frac{x \sqrt{x^2 + a^2}}{2} + \frac{a^2}{2} \ln (x + \sqrt{x^2 + a^2}) - \frac{a^2}{2} \ln a + C$$
(See $\int 23$)

127 Let $u = \sqrt{2}\, x$; $du = \sqrt{2} \, dx$.

$$\int = \frac{1}{\sqrt{2}} \int \frac{du}{\sqrt{u^2 + 5}} = \frac{1}{\sqrt{2}} \ln (u + \sqrt{u^2 + 5}) + C \Big|^{u=\sqrt{2}x}$$

$$= \frac{1}{\sqrt{2}} \ln (\sqrt{2}\, x + \sqrt{2x^2 + 5}) + C$$

128 $\displaystyle\int \frac{dx}{x \sqrt{x^2 - a^2}} = ?$ Note the expression $x^2 - a^2$ in the integrand.
By the remark in item 2, following Frame **116c**, this suggests the second change-of-variable technique with $x = a \sec t$.   The natural form of the inverse function is $t = \text{arcsec}\ (x/a)$, but since we have not introduced the arcsec function, we may write instead $t = \arccos\ (a/x)$, as justified by: $x/a = \sec t$; $a/x = \cos t$.   Under this procedure the six trigonometric functions of t may be read from the triangle:

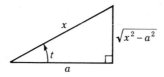

129 $\displaystyle\int \frac{\sqrt{x^2 - a^2}}{x}\, dx\ = ?$

130 Apply ∫28 to evaluate $\displaystyle\int \frac{\sqrt{5x^2 - 3}}{x}\, dx.$

128 Let $x = a \sec t$; then $dx = a \sec t \tan t \, dt$ and the inverse function is $t = \arccos (a/x)$.

$$\int = \int \frac{a \sec t \tan t}{a \sec t \sqrt{a^2 \tan^2 t}} \, dt \Big|^{t=\arccos \, (a/x)}$$

$$= \frac{1}{a} \int dt = \frac{1}{a} t + C \Big|^{t=\arccos \, (a/x)}$$

$$= \frac{1}{a} \arccos \frac{a}{x} + C \qquad \text{(See } \smallint 25)$$

129 Let $x = a \sec t$; $dx = a \sec t \tan t \, dt$, $t = \operatorname{arcsec} (x/a) = \arccos (a/x)$.

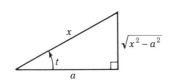

$$\int = \int \frac{\sqrt{a^2 \tan^2 t}}{a \sec t} \, a \sec t \tan t \, dt \Big|^{t=\arccos \, (a/x)}$$

$$= a \int \tan^2 t \, dt = a \int (\sec^2 t - 1) \, dt$$

$$= a \tan t - at + C \big|^{t=\arccos \, (a/x)}$$

$$= \sqrt{x^2 - a^2} - a \arccos \frac{a}{x} + C \qquad \text{(See } \smallint 28)$$

130 Let $u = \sqrt{5} \, x$, $du = \sqrt{5} \, dx$.

$$\int = \int \frac{\sqrt{u^2 - 3}}{u} \, du \Big|^{u=\sqrt{5}x}$$

$$= \sqrt{u^2 - 3} - \sqrt{3} \arccos \frac{\sqrt{3}}{u} + C \Big|^{u=\sqrt{5}x}$$

$$= \sqrt{5x^2 - 3} - \sqrt{3} \arccos \frac{\sqrt{3}}{\sqrt{5} \, x} + C$$

131 $\int \dfrac{dx}{\sqrt{(x^2 - a^2)^3}} = ?$

This is an algebraic interlude. A *rational function* is a quotient of two polynomials. Our purpose is to develop procedures for the integration of rational functions.

1 We need only consider rational functions for which the polynomial in the numerator has degree less than that of the denominator. Otherwise, by division, a rational function can be written as a polynomial added to a rational function which satisfies this condition. For example,

$$\frac{3x^3 + 4x^2 - 9x - 5}{x^2 - x} = 3x + 7 - \frac{2x + 5}{x^2 - x}$$

2 As a result of the theory of equations, every polynomial can be written as a product of linear and quadratic polynomials (i.e., polynomials of the first and second degrees). We assume this result. For example,

$$x^3 - 1 = (x - 1)(x^2 + x + 1)$$
$$x^4 - 1 = (x - 1)(x + 1)(x^2 + 1)$$
$$x^8 - 2x^4 + 1 = (x^4 - 1)^2 = (x - 1)^2(x + 1)^2(x^2 + 1)^2$$

However the task of finding such factors may be considerable, and, since we do not wish to labor the algebraic difficulties here, we will limit ourselves to instances where such factors are easily recognizable.

3 The procedure called *partial fractions* involves the writing of a rational function (where the degree of the numerator polynomial is less than that of the denominator polynomial) as a sum of simpler fractions. We assume, specifically, that if p is the highest power of a linear factor of the denominator, then the sum will include p terms involving this linear factor, as follows:

$$\frac{[\quad]}{[\quad](a + bx)^p} = \frac{A_1}{a + bx} + \frac{A_2}{(a + bx)^2} + \cdots + \frac{A_p}{(a + bx)^p} + [\quad]$$

131   Let $x = a \sec t; dx = a \sec t \tan t \, dt, t = \mathrm{arcsec}\ (x/a) = \mathrm{arccos}\ (a/x).$

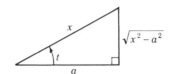

$$\int = \int (a^2 \tan^2 t)^{-\frac{3}{2}} a \sec t \tan t \, dt \Big|^{t=\mathrm{arccos}\ (a/x)}$$

$$= \frac{1}{a^2} \int \frac{\sec t}{\tan^2 t} \, dt$$

$$= \frac{1}{a^2} \int \frac{1}{\sin^2 t} \cos t \, dt = -\frac{1}{a^2} \csc t + C \Big|^{t=\mathrm{arccos}\ (a/x)}$$

$$= \frac{-x}{a^2 \sqrt{x^2 - a^2}} + C \qquad \text{(See } \int 31)$$

where each A_i is a constant. We assume, also, that if p is the highest power of a quadratic factor of the denominator, then the sum will include p terms involving these quadratic factors, as follows:

$$\frac{[\quad]}{[\quad](a + bx + cx^2)^p} = \frac{A_1 + B_1 x}{a + bx + cx^2} + \frac{A_2 + B_2 x}{(a + bx + cx^2)^2}$$

$$+ \cdots + \frac{A_p + B_p x}{(a + bx + cx^2)^p} + [\quad]$$

where each A_i and B_i are constants. For example the following rational function can be written as a sum of fractions in the following form:

$$\frac{[\quad]}{x(1 + 2x)(3 + 4x)^3(5 + 6x + 7x^2)^2} = \frac{A}{x} + \frac{B}{1 + 2x} + \frac{C}{3 + 4x}$$

$$+ \frac{D}{(3 + 4x)^2} + \frac{E}{(3 + 4x)^3} + \frac{F + Gx}{5 + 6x + 7x^2} + \frac{H + Ix}{(5 + 6x + 7x^2)^2}$$

132 Write the following as the sum of partial fractions with undetermined constants as specified.

a $\dfrac{2 + x}{(1 - x)(1 + x)}$.

b $\dfrac{2 + x^2}{(1 - x)(1 + x)^2}$. Note that the denominator is a product of linear factors.

c $\dfrac{2 + x^2}{(1 - x)^2(1 + x)^3}$.

d $\dfrac{2 + x^2}{(1 - x)(1 + x + x^2)}$. Note the quadratic factor in the denominator.

e $\dfrac{2 + x^2}{(1 - x)(1 + 2x + x^2)}$.

132 a $\dfrac{A}{1-x} + \dfrac{B}{1+x}$

b $\dfrac{A}{1-x} + \dfrac{B}{1+x} + \dfrac{C}{(1+x)^2}$

c $\dfrac{A}{1-x} + \dfrac{B}{(1-x)^2} + \dfrac{C}{1+x} + \dfrac{D}{(1+x)^2} + \dfrac{E}{(1+x)^3}$

d See item 3, following Frame **131**; partial fractions resulting from quadratic factors have *linear* (first-degree) numerators.

$$\frac{2+x^2}{(1-x)(1+x+x^2)} = \frac{A}{1-x} + \frac{B+Cx}{1+x+x^2}$$

e The polynomial $1 + 2x + x^2$ is factorable into $(1+x)^2$. Hence, see Frame **132b**.

f $\dfrac{2 + x^2}{(1 - x)(1 + x + x^2)^2}.$

g $\dfrac{2 + x^2}{(1 - x^2)(1 + x^2)^2}.$

h $\dfrac{2 + x^2}{(1 + x^2)^2(1 + 3x^2)^3}.$

Once the structure of the partial fractions has been exhibited, we need determine the constants appearing in the numerators. This is done by solving a system of linear equations and can get messy when the degree of the denominator polynomial is large. The procedure depends on the consequence of the *fundamental theorem of algebra* that a polynomial equation of degree n can have no more than n distinct solutions. Thus, for example, if we know that $a + bx + cx^2 = 0$ for more than two distinct numbers x, then $a = b = c = 0$. It follows that if two polynomials in x of degree n are equal for more than n values of x, then their corresponding coefficients are equal. That is, if $a + bx + cx^2 = A + Bx + Cx^2$ for more than two distinct values of x, then $a = A$ and $b = B$ and $c = C$. We illustrate the procedure in the following frames.

---

133 **a** Write $\dfrac{5 - x}{1 - x^2}$ as the sum of partial fractions with undetermined constants.

b Now add the two partial fractions and equate their sum to the original rational function.

c Now equate the corresponding coefficients of the two polynomials and solve the resulting system of linear equations (in A and B).

f $\dfrac{A}{1-x} + \dfrac{B+Cx}{1+x+x^2} + \dfrac{D+Ex}{(1+x+x^2)^2}.$

g $(1-x^2)$ is factorable into $(1-x)(1+x)$. Hence:

$$\dfrac{A}{1-x} + \dfrac{B}{1+x} + \dfrac{C+Dx}{1+x^2} + \dfrac{E+Fx}{(1+x^2)^2}.$$

h $\dfrac{A+Bx}{1+x^2} + \dfrac{C+Dx}{(1+x^2)^2} + \dfrac{E+Fx}{1+3x^2} + \dfrac{G+Hx}{(1+3x^2)^2} + \dfrac{I+Jx}{(1+3x^2)^3}$

133 a $\dfrac{5-x}{1-x^2} = \dfrac{5-x}{(1-x)(1+x)} = \dfrac{A}{1-x} + \dfrac{B}{1+x}$

b $\dfrac{A}{1-x} + \dfrac{B}{1+x} = \dfrac{A(1+x) + B(1-x)}{1-x^2}$

$$= \dfrac{(A+B) + (A-B)x}{1-x^2} = \dfrac{5-x}{1-x^2}$$

Thus $(A+B) + (A-B)x = 5-x$, for almost all x, i.e., for all $x \neq \pm 1$, the values for which the denominators are zero.

c $\begin{cases} A+B = 5 \\ A-B = -1 \end{cases}$ $\quad 2A = 4; A = 2; B = 3$

Thus $\dfrac{5-x}{1-x^2} = \dfrac{2}{1-x} + \dfrac{3}{1+x}$, and we have written the given rational function as the sum of partial fractions with *determined* numerators.

134 a Write $\dfrac{2 + 3x}{2x - x^2 - x^3}$ as the sum of partial fractions with undetermined constants.

b Now, add the three partial fractions and, as in Frame **133**, determine the constants A, B, C.

135 Write as a sum of partial fractions $\dfrac{2x + 1}{x(x - 1)^2}$.

136 Write as a sum of partial fractions $\dfrac{3 + 4x^2}{x(1 + x^2)}$.

134 **a** $\dfrac{2 + 3x}{2x - x^2 - x^3} = \dfrac{2 + 3x}{x(2 + x)(1 - x)} = \dfrac{A}{x} + \dfrac{B}{2 + x} + \dfrac{C}{1 - x}$

b $\dfrac{A}{x} + \dfrac{B}{2 + x} + \dfrac{C}{1 - x}$

$$= \dfrac{A(2 + x)(1 - x) + Bx(1 - x) + Cx(2 + x)}{x(2 + x)(1 - x)}$$

$$= \dfrac{2A + (-A + B + 2C)x + (-A - B + C)x^2}{x(2 + x)(1 - x)}$$

$$= \dfrac{2 + 3x}{x(2 + x)(1 - x)}$$

Thus

$$\begin{cases} 2A = 2 \\ -A + B + 2C = 3 \\ -A - B + C = 0 \end{cases} \quad \begin{cases} A = 1 \\ B = \frac{2}{3} \\ C = \frac{5}{3} \end{cases}$$

$$\dfrac{2 + 3x}{2x - x^2 - x^3} = \dfrac{1}{x} + \dfrac{2}{3(2 + x)} + \dfrac{5}{3(1 - x)}.$$

135 $\dfrac{2x + 1}{x(x - 1)^2} = \dfrac{A}{x} + \dfrac{B}{x - 1} + \dfrac{C}{(x - 1)^2}$

$2x + 1 = A(x - 1)^2 + Bx(x - 1) + Cx$

$\qquad = (A + B)x^2 + (-2A - B + C)x + A$

$A + B = 0, \ -2A - B + C = 2, \ A = 1; \ A = 1, \ B = -1, \ C = 3;$

$$\dfrac{2x + 1}{x(x - 1)^2} = \dfrac{1}{x} - \dfrac{1}{x - 1} + \dfrac{3}{(x - 1)^2}$$

136 $\dfrac{3 + 4x^2}{x(1 + x^2)} = \dfrac{A}{x} + \dfrac{B + Cx}{1 + x^2}$

$\qquad 3 + 4x^2 = A(1 + x^2) + (B + Cx)x = A + Bx + (A + C)x^2$

$\qquad A = 3, \ B = 0, \ A + C = 4; \ C = 1;$

$$\dfrac{3 + 4x^2}{x(1 + x^2)} = \dfrac{3}{x} + \dfrac{x}{1 + x^2}$$

137 Write as a sum of partial fractions $\dfrac{1 - x + x^2}{x(1 + x^2)^2}$.

When a rational function is written as the sum of partial fractions, each such fraction is of the form $\dfrac{A}{(a + bx)^n}$ or $\dfrac{A + Bx}{(a + bx + cx^2)^n}$, and the fraction on the right can in turn be written as the sum of the two fractions

$$\frac{A}{(a + bx + cx^2)^n} + \frac{Bx}{(a + bx + cx^2)^n}$$

Thus every rational function (with denominator factored) can be integrated, providing we can integrate each of the following: $\dfrac{1}{(a + bx)^n}$, $\dfrac{1}{(a + bx + cx^2)^n}$, $\dfrac{x}{(a + bx + cx^2)^n}$. Integral formulas for the first of these is given by $\int 5$ and $\int 6$; for the second by $\int 15$ and $\int 17$; and for the third by $\int 18$ and $\int 19$. We proceed to develop these formulas.

---

138 $\int (a + bx)^n \, dx = ?$ $(b \neq 0)$

139 Apply $\int 6$ to evaluate $\displaystyle\int \frac{dx}{2 + 3x}$.

140 Apply $\int 5$ to evaluate $\displaystyle\int \frac{dx}{(2 + 3x)^3}$.

137
$$\frac{1 - x + x^2}{x(1 + x^2)^2} = \frac{A}{x} + \frac{B + Cx}{1 + x^2} + \frac{D + Ex}{(1 + x^2)^2}$$

$$\begin{aligned} 1 - x + x^2 &= A(1 + x^2)^2 + (B + Cx)x(1 + x^2) + (D + Ex)x \\ &= A + (B + D)x + (2A + C + E)x^2 + Bx^3 \\ &\qquad\qquad\qquad\qquad\qquad\qquad\qquad + (A + C)x^4 \end{aligned}$$

$A = 1,\ B + D = -1,\ 2A + C + E = 1,\ B = 0,\ A + C = 0;$

$A = 1,\ B = 0,\ D = -1,\ C = -1,\ E = 0;$

$$\frac{1 - x + x^2}{x(1 + x^2)^2} = \frac{1}{x} - \frac{x}{1 + x^2} - \frac{1}{(1 + x^2)^2}$$

138 Let $u = a + bx$; then $du = b\,dx$.

$$\int (a + bx)^n\,dx = \frac{1}{b}\int u^n\,du \Big|^{u=a+bx}$$

$$= \frac{u^{n+1}}{b(n + 1)} + C \Big|^{u=a+bx}$$

$$= \frac{(a + bx)^{n+1}}{b(n + 1)} + C \qquad \text{if } n \neq -1$$

$$\int = \frac{1}{b}\ln u + C \Big|^{u=a+bx}$$

$$= \frac{1}{b}\ln (a + bx) + C \qquad \text{if } n = -1 \qquad (\text{See } \textstyle\int 5 \text{ and } \int 6)$$

139 $\int = \frac{1}{3}\ln (2 + 3x) + C$

140 Replace n by -3.

$$\int = \frac{1}{3}\frac{(a + bx)^{-2}}{-2} + C = \frac{-1}{6(a + bx)^2} + C$$

We are going to cheat a little in the development of formula $\int 15$; its proper development requires first an application of the algebraic technique called *completing the square*, then a trigonometric substitution, and, finally, an evaluation of the resulting trigonometric integrand. Instead we will merely check this formula by differentiation.

141   If $X = a + bx + cx^2$ and $q = 4ac - b^2 > 0$, show that

$$D_x\left(\frac{2}{\sqrt{q}}\arctan\frac{2cx + b}{\sqrt{q}}\right) = \frac{1}{X}.$$

142   **a**   We will check $\int 17$ by differentiation.   First, with

$$X = a + bx + cx^2$$

and

$$q = 4ac - b^2,$$

show that

$$4cX - q = (b + 2cx)^2.$$

b   Now utilizing Frame **142a**, show that

$$D_x\frac{b + 2cx}{X^n} = \frac{nq}{X^{n+1}} - \frac{2(2n - 1)c}{X^n}.$$

143   **a**   With $X = a + bx + cx^2$, evaluate $\displaystyle\int\frac{b + 2cx}{X}\,dx.$

b   Write $\displaystyle\int\frac{b + 2cx}{X}\,dx = b\int\frac{dx}{X} + 2c\int\frac{x}{X}\,dx,$ and **apply Frame 143a** to derive $\int 18$.

141 $\quad D\left(\dfrac{2}{\sqrt{q}}\arctan\dfrac{2cx+b}{\sqrt{q}}\right) = \dfrac{2}{\sqrt{q}}\dfrac{1}{1+\left(\dfrac{2cx+b}{\sqrt{q}}\right)^2}\dfrac{2c}{\sqrt{q}}$

$$= \ldots = \dfrac{1}{X}$$

Thus ∫15. For our purposes here we need not consider the case $q \le 0$, for in that case the quadratic $a + bx + cx^2$ is factorable into linear factors.

142   **a** $4cX - q = 4c(a + bx + cx^2) - (4ac - b^2)$

$$= 4ac + 4bcx + 4c^2x^2 - 4ac + b^2$$

$$= b^2 + 4bcx + 4c^2x^2 = (b + 2cx)^2$$

  b $D\dfrac{b + 2cx}{X^n} = \dfrac{X^n 2c - (b + 2cx)nX^{n-1}(b + 2cx)}{X^{2n}}$

$$= \dfrac{2cX - n(b + 2cx)^2}{X^{n+1}}$$

$$= \dfrac{2cX - n4cX + nq}{X^{n+1}} \qquad \text{(by Frame 142a)}$$

$$= \dfrac{-2c(2n - 1)}{X^n} + \dfrac{nq}{X^{n+1}}$$

Writing this as an integral formula and dividing by nq, we have ∫17.

143   **a**   Let $u = X = a + bx + cx^2$, then $du = (b + 2cx)\,dx$.

$$\int \dfrac{b + 2cx}{X}\,dx = \int \dfrac{du}{u}\Big|_{u=X} = \ln u + C\Big|_{u=X} = \ln X + C$$

  b   By substitution from Frame **143a**,

$$\ln X = b\int \dfrac{dx}{X} + 2c\int \dfrac{x}{X}\,dx$$

$$2c\int \dfrac{x}{X}\,dx = \ln X - b\int \dfrac{dx}{X}$$

$$\int \dfrac{x}{X}\,dx = \dfrac{1}{2c}\ln X - \dfrac{b}{2c}\int \dfrac{dx}{X}$$

c   With $X = a + bx + cx^2$, evaluate $\int \dfrac{b + 2cx}{X^{n+1}}\, dx$.

d   Write $\int \dfrac{b + 2cx}{X^{n+1}}\, dx = b \int \dfrac{dx}{X^{n+1}} + 2c \int \dfrac{x}{X^{n+1}}\, dx$, then apply Frame **143c** and $\int 17$ to derive $\int 19$.

144 $\int \dfrac{5 - x}{1 - x^2}\, dx = ?$ This integrand is a rational function; it can be written as the sum of partial fractions (see Frame **133c**).

145 $\int \dfrac{2 + 3x}{2x - x^2 - x^3}\, dx = ?$ (see Frame **134b**)

c Let $u = X = a + bx + cx^2$; then $du = (b + 2cx)\,dx$.

$$\int = \int \frac{du}{u^{n+1}} \Big|^{u=X} = \int u^{-n-1}\,du$$

$$= \frac{u^{-n}}{-n} + C \Big|^{u=X} = \frac{-1}{nX^n} + C$$

d
$$-\frac{1}{nX^n} = b\int \frac{dx}{X^{n+1}} + 2c\int \frac{x}{X^{n+1}}\,dx$$

$$= -\frac{1}{nX^n} - b\int \frac{dx}{X^{n+1}}$$

$$= \frac{-1}{nX^n} - \frac{b(b + 2cx)}{nqX^n} + \frac{2b(2n - 1)c}{qn}\int \frac{dx}{X^n}$$

$$\int \frac{x}{X^{n+1}}\,dx = \frac{-4ac + 2bcx}{2cnqX^n} - \frac{b(2n - 1)}{qn}\int \frac{dx}{X^n}$$

144 By Frame **133c**,

$$\int \frac{5 - x}{1 - x^2}\,dx = 2\int \frac{1}{1 - x}\,dx + 3\int \frac{1}{1 + x}\,dx$$

$$= -2\int \frac{du}{u}\Big|^{u=1-x} + 3\int \frac{dv}{v}\Big|^{v=1+x}$$

$$= -2\ln(1 - x) + 3\ln(1 + x) + C$$

$$= \ln \frac{(1 + x)^3}{(1 - x)^2} + C.$$

Or, the two integrals of the partial fractions could be evaluated by ∫6.

145 $$\int \frac{2 + 3x}{2x - x^2 - x^3}\,dx = \int \frac{dx}{x} + \frac{2}{3}\int \frac{dx}{2 + x} + \frac{5}{3}\int \frac{dx}{1 - x}$$

$$= \ln x + \tfrac{2}{3}\ln(2 + x) - \tfrac{5}{3}\ln(1 - x) + C$$

$$= \ln \frac{x(2 + x)^{\frac{2}{3}}}{(1 - x)^{\frac{5}{3}}} + C$$

146 $\displaystyle\int \frac{2x + 1}{x(x - 1)^2}\, dx = ?$ (see Frame **135**)

147 $\displaystyle\int \frac{3 + 4x^2}{x + x^3}\, dx = ?$ (see Frame **136**)

148 $\displaystyle\int \frac{1 - x + x^2}{x(1 + x^2)^2}\, dx = ?$ (see Frame **137**)

146 $\displaystyle\int \frac{2x+1}{x(x-1)^2}\, dx = \int \frac{dx}{x} - \int \frac{dx}{x-1} + 3 \int \frac{dx}{(x-1)^2}$

$$= \ln x - \int \frac{du}{u}\bigg|^{u=x-1} + 3 \int \frac{du}{u^2}\bigg|^{u=x-1}$$

$$= \ln x - \ln (x-1) - \frac{3}{x-1} + C$$

Or, the integrals of the partial fractions could be evaluated by ∫5 and ∫6. When powers of linear factors appear in the partial fractions, these are easily evaluated, almost by recognition; when powers of quadratic factors appear, we suggest applying ∫15, ∫17, ∫18, ∫19 if they are not immediately recognized.

147 $\displaystyle\int \frac{3+4x^2}{x+x^3}\, dx = 3 \int \frac{dx}{x} + \int \frac{x\, dx}{1+x^2}$

$$= 3 \ln x + \frac{1}{2} \int \frac{du}{u}\bigg|^{u=1+x^2}$$

$$= 3 \ln x + \tfrac{1}{2} \ln (1+x^2) + C$$

$$= \ln (x^3 \sqrt{1+x^2}) + C$$

The integral $\displaystyle\int \frac{x}{1+x^2}\, dx$ could be written as $\displaystyle\int \frac{x\, dx}{X}$ where $X = 1 + x^2$; i.e., a replaced by 1, b by 0, c by 1. Thus, ∫18, $\int = \tfrac{1}{2} \ln (1+x^2) - 0$.

148 $\displaystyle\int \frac{1-x+x^2}{x(1+x^2)^2}\, dx = \int \frac{dx}{x} - \int \frac{x\, dx}{1+x^2} - \int \frac{dx}{(1+x^2)^2}$

$$\int \frac{dx}{x} = \ln x$$

$$\int \frac{x\, dx}{1+x^2} = \frac{1}{2} \int \frac{1}{u}\, du\bigg|^{u=x^2+1}$$

$$= \tfrac{1}{2} \ln u\big|^{u=x^2+1} = \tfrac{1}{2} \ln (x^2+1)$$

$$\int \frac{dx}{(1+x^2)^2} = \frac{2x}{4(1+x^2)} + \frac{2}{4} \int \frac{dx}{1+x^2} = \frac{x}{2(1+x^2)} + \frac{1}{2} \arctan x$$

(by ∫16, which is the $n = 1$ instance of ∫17, with $X = 1 + x^2$, $a = 1$, $b = 0$, $c = 1$, thus $q = 4$).

Thus

$$\int \frac{1-x+x^2}{x(1+x^2)^2}\, dx = \ln x - \frac{1}{2} \ln (1+x^2) - \frac{x}{2(1+x^2)}$$
$$- \tfrac{1}{2} \arctan x + C.$$

149 $\displaystyle\int \frac{x^2}{1+x}\,dx = ?$

150 $\displaystyle\int \frac{1}{x^2(1+x+x^2)^2}\,dx = ?$

149 The integrand is a rational function, but the degree of the denominator is less than that of the numerator. Thus, by division,

$$\frac{x^2}{1+x} = x - 1 + \frac{1}{1+x}$$

and

$$\int \frac{x^2}{1+x}\, dx = \frac{1}{2}x^2 - x + \ln(1+x) + C.$$

150 First, determine partial fractions.

$$\frac{1}{x^2(1+x+x^2)^2} = \frac{A}{x} + \frac{B}{x^2} + \frac{C+Dx}{1+x+x^2} + \frac{E+Fx}{(1+x+x^2)^2}$$
$$1 = Ax(1+x+x^2)^2 + B(1+x+x^2)^2 + (C+Dx)x^2(1+x+x^2)$$
$$+ (E+Fx)x^2;$$
$$1 = B + (A+2B)x + (2A+3B+C+E)x^2$$
$$+ (3A+2B+C+D+F)x^3 + (2A+B+C+D)x^4$$
$$+ (A+D)x^5;$$

$$B = 1,\quad A + 2B = 0,\quad 2A + 3B + C + E = 0,$$
$$3A + 2B + C + D + F = 0,\; 2A + B + C + D = 0,\; A + D = 0;$$
$$B = 1, A = -2, D = 2, C = 1, E = 0, F = 1;$$
$$\frac{1}{x^2(1+x+x^2)^2} = -\frac{2}{x} + \frac{1}{x^2} + \frac{1+2x}{1+x+x^2} + \frac{x}{(1+x+x^2)^2}$$
$$\int \frac{1+2x}{1+x+x^2}\, dx = [\text{letting } X = 1+x+x^2;\; dX = (2x+1)\, dx]$$
$$= \int \frac{dX}{X}\Big|^{X=1+x+x^2} = \ln(1+x+x^2)$$

and, with X above, we have

$$\int \frac{x\, dx}{X^2} = -\frac{x+2}{3X} - \frac{1}{3}\int \frac{dx}{X} = -\frac{x+2}{3X} - \frac{1}{3}\frac{2}{\sqrt{3}}\arctan\frac{2x+1}{\sqrt{3}}.$$

Hence:

$$\int \frac{dx}{x^2(1+x+x^2)^2} = -2\ln x - \frac{1}{x} + \ln(1+x+x^2)$$
$$- \frac{x+2}{3(1+x+x^2)} - \frac{2}{3\sqrt{3}}\arctan\frac{2x+1}{\sqrt{3}} + C.$$

151 In each of the following indicate the first significant step you would take in attempting to integrate. In particular:

1. If you recognize the antiderivative, evaluate.
2. If a change of variables is to be made, indicate the precise replacement but do not evaluate.
3. If integration by parts is indicated, write $u = ?$ $dv = ?$
4. If the partial-fraction technique is indicated, write the integrand as the sum of partial fractions with undetermined coefficients.

a $\int (2 + e^x)^{\frac{3}{2}} e^x \, dx = ?$

b $\int \dfrac{\sin x}{2 + \cos x} \, dx = ?$

c $\int x^2 \sin x \, dx = ?$

d $\int \dfrac{1}{(x + 1)(x - 1)^2} \, dx = ?$

e $\int \dfrac{\ln^3 x}{x} \, dx = ?$

f $\int \cos^2 2x \, dx = ?$

g $\int x^3 \sqrt{x + 1} \, dx = ?$

h $\int \dfrac{\sqrt{x + 1}}{\sqrt{x - 1}} \, dx = ?$

i $\int \sin^4 x \cos^3 x \, dx = ?$

j $\int \sqrt{3 - x^2} \, dx = ?$

k $\int \dfrac{dx}{x \sqrt{3 + 5x^2}} = ?$

l $\int \dfrac{dx}{x \sqrt{3 + 5x}} = ?$

m $\int \arcsin x \, dx = ?$

151 a By recognition, $\int = \frac{2}{5}(2 + e)^{\frac{5}{2}} + C$, or by change of variables $u = 2 + e^x$, $du = e^x \, dx$. Also acceptable is the change of variables $u = e^x$.

b By recognition or by change of variables, $u = 2 + \cos x$ or $u = \cos x$, $du = -\sin x \, dx$.

c Integration by parts: $u = x^2$, $dv = \sin x \, dx$.

d Partial fractions, with integrand written as

$$\frac{A}{x + 1} + \frac{B}{x - 1} + \frac{C}{(x - 1)^2}.$$

e Change of variables: let $u = \ln x$, $du = \dfrac{1}{x} \, dx$.

f Write $\cos^2 2x = \frac{1}{2}(1 + \cos 4x)$.

g Change of variables: $x = t^2 - 1$, $dx = 2t \, dt$, $t = \sqrt{x + 1}$.

h Change of variables: $x = t^2$, $dx = 2t \, dt$, $t = \sqrt{x}$.

i Write $\cos^3 x = \cos^2 x \cdot \cos x = (1 - \sin^2 x) \cos x$, then change of variables: $u = \sin x$, $du = \cos x \, dx$.

j Change of variables: let $x = \sqrt{3} \sin t$, $dx = \sqrt{3} \cos t \, dt$, $t = \arcsin (x/\sqrt{3})$.

k Change of variables: let $x = \sqrt{\frac{3}{5}} \tan t$, $dx = \sqrt{\frac{3}{5}} \sec^2 t \, dt$, $t = \arctan \sqrt{\frac{5}{3}} \, x$.

l Change of variables: $x = \frac{1}{5}(t^2 - 3)$, $dx = \frac{2}{5}t \, dt$, $t = \sqrt{3 + 5x}$.

m Integration by parts: $u = \arcsin x$, $dv = 1 \, dx$

n $\int \dfrac{x\,dx}{(a^2 + x^2)^{\frac{3}{2}}} = ?$

o $\int \dfrac{x^3}{(a^2 + x^2)^{\frac{3}{2}}}\,dx = ?$

p $\int \sec^4 x\,dx = ?$

q $\int \tan^3 x \sec x\,dx = ?$

r $\int \dfrac{x^2 - 1}{x^2 + 1}\,dx = ?$

s $\int \ln (1 + x^2)\,dx = ?$

t $\int \dfrac{dx}{x^2(1 + x^2)^3} = ?$

152 $\int \dfrac{x^2\,dx}{a + bx} = ?$ Let $u = a + bx$ in order to simplify the denominator.

153 Forms containing $\sqrt{a + bx}$ may be integrable by the change of variables motivated by $t = \sqrt{a + bx}$, i.e., $x = \dfrac{1}{b}\,(t^2 - a)$, $dx = \dfrac{2t}{b}\,dt$. Apply this technique to evaluate $\int x^2\,\sqrt{a + bx}\,dx$.

n Change of variables: let $u = a^2 + x^2$, $du = 2x\,dx$; or let $x = a \tan t$, $dx = a \sec^2 t\,dt$, $t = \arctan(x/a)$.

o Change of variables: let $x = a \tan t$, $dx = a \sec^2 t\,dt$, $t = \arctan (x/a)$; or let $x = \sqrt{t^2 - a^2}$, $dx = (t^2 - a^2)^{-\frac{1}{2}}t\,dt$, $t = \sqrt{a^2 + x^2}$.

p Write $\sec^4 x = \sec^2 x \cdot \sec^2 x = (1 + \tan^2 x)\sec^2 x$, then let $u = \tan x$, $du = \sec^2 x\,dx$. Or apply reduction formula $\int 59$.

q Write $\tan^3 x \cdot \sec x = \tan^2 x \cdot \sec x \cdot \tan x = (\sec^2 x - 1)\sec x \cdot \tan x$, then let $u = \sec x$, $du = \sec x \cdot \tan x\,dx$.

r Rational function, but degree of denominator does not exceed that of numerator. First divide: $\dfrac{x^2 - 1}{x^2 + 1} = 1 - \dfrac{2}{x^2 + 1}$.

s Integration by parts: $u = \ln(1 + x^2)$, $dv = 1\,dx$.

t Partial fractions with integrand written as
$$\frac{A}{x} + \frac{B}{x^2} + \frac{C + Dx}{1 + x^2} + \frac{E + Fx}{(1 + x^2)^2} + \frac{G + Hx}{(1 + x^2)^3}$$

152 Let $u = a + bx$, $du = b\,dx$. Note, then, that $x = \dfrac{1}{b}(u - a)$.

$$\int = \frac{1}{b^3}\int \frac{(u - a)^2}{u}\,du \Big|^{u=a+bx}$$
$$= \frac{1}{b^3}\int \left(u - 2a + \frac{a^2}{u}\right)du$$
$$= \frac{1}{b^3}\left(\frac{1}{2}u^2 - 2au + a^2 \ln u\right) + C \Big|^{u=a+bx}$$
$$= \frac{1}{b^3}\left[\frac{1}{2}(a + bx)^2 - 2a(a + bx) + a^2 \ln(a + bx)\right] + C$$

See $\int 7$. Integrands containing $(a + bx)$ may succumb to this change of variables.

153 $\displaystyle\int x^2 \sqrt{a + bx}\,dx = \frac{2}{b^3}\int (t^2 - a)^2 t^2\,dt \Big|^{t=\sqrt{a+bx}}$
$$= \frac{2}{b^3}\int (t^6 - 2at^4 + a^2 t^2)\,dt$$
$$= \frac{2}{b^3}\left(\frac{t^7}{7} - \frac{2at^5}{5} + \frac{a^2 t^3}{3}\right) + C \Big|^{t=\sqrt{a+bx}}$$
$$= (\text{see } \int 21)$$

154 a Quadratic expressions which are the sums or differences of squares $(x^2 \pm a^2, a^2 - x^2)$, are amenable to the trigonometric-substitutions suggested in the remark following Frame **116c**. Illustrate this procedure by evaluating $\int \sqrt{a^2 - x^2}\, dx$.

b Apply ∫35 to evaluate $\int \sqrt{5 - 2x^2}\, dx$. First, let $u = \sqrt{2}x$ in order to attain the form of ∫35.

155 a Quadratic expressions can be converted into the sum or difference of squares by the algebraic procedure of completing the square. For example,

$$x^2 - 2x = (x^2 - 2x + 1) - 1 = (x - 1)^2 - 1^2.$$

Write each of the following as the sum or difference of squares of linear or constant terms:

(1) $x^2 - 3x$ (2) $4x^2 + 3x + 1$ (3) $2x - x^2$
(4) $3x^2 + x + 1$ (5) $1 - x - 3x^2$

154 **a** Let $x = a \sin t$, $dx = a \cos t \, dt$, $t = \arcsin (x/a)$.

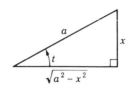

$$\int \sqrt{a^2 - x^2} \, dx = a^2 \int \cos^2 t \, dt \Big|^{t=\arcsin \,(x/a)}$$

$$= \frac{a^2}{2} \int (1 + \cos 2t) \, dt$$

$$= \frac{a^2}{2} t + \frac{a^2}{4} \sin 2t + C$$

$$= \frac{a^2}{2} t + \frac{a^2}{2} \sin t \cos t + C \Big|^{t=\arcsin \,(x/a)}$$

$$= \frac{a^2}{2} \arcsin \frac{x}{a} + \frac{x \sqrt{a^2 - x^2}}{2} + C \qquad \text{(See } \int 35)$$

b $\displaystyle \int \sqrt{5 - 2x^2} \, dx = \frac{1}{\sqrt{2}} \int \sqrt{5 - u^2} \, du \Big|^{u=\sqrt{2}\,x}$

$$= \frac{1}{2\sqrt{2}} \left(u \sqrt{5 - u^2} + 5 \arcsin \frac{u}{\sqrt{5}} \right) + C \Big|^{u=\sqrt{2}\,x}$$

$$\text{(by } \int 35 \text{ with } a = \sqrt{5})$$

$$= \frac{1}{2\sqrt{2}} \left(\sqrt{2}\,x \sqrt{5 - 2x^2} + 5 \arcsin \frac{\sqrt{2}\,x}{\sqrt{5}} \right) + C$$

155 **a** (1) $x^2 - 3x = (x^2 - 3x + \frac{9}{4}) - \frac{9}{4} = (x - \frac{3}{2})^2 - (\frac{3}{2})^2$

(2) $4x^2 + 3x + 1 = (4x^2 + 3x + \frac{9}{16}) + (1 - \frac{9}{16})$

$$= \left(2x + \frac{3}{4} \right)^2 + \left(\frac{\sqrt{7}}{4} \right)^2$$

(3) $2x - x^2 = 1 - (x^2 - 2x + 1) = 1^2 - (x - 1)^2$

(4) $3x^2 + x + 1 = (3x^2 + x + \frac{1}{12}) + (1 - \frac{1}{12})$

$$= \left(\sqrt{3x} + \frac{1}{2\sqrt{3}} \right)^2 + \left(\sqrt{\frac{11}{12}} \right)^2$$

(5) $1 - x - 3x^2 = (1 + \frac{1}{12}) - (3x^2 + x + \frac{1}{12})$

$$= \left(\sqrt{\frac{13}{12}} \right)^2 - \left(\sqrt{3x} + \frac{1}{2\sqrt{3}} \right)^2$$

b Once a quadratic expression is written as a sum or difference of squares, the resulting integrand may suggest a suitable trigonometric substitution or an application of one of the integral formulas ∫23 to ∫46. As an illustration, evaluate $\displaystyle\int \frac{1}{\sqrt{2x - x^2}} \, dx$.

c Evaluate $\displaystyle\int \frac{dx}{(2x - x^2)^{\frac{3}{2}}}$.

d Evaluate $\displaystyle\int \sqrt{4x^2 + 3x + 1} \, dx$.

b First, $2x - x^2 = 1 - (x - 1)^2$. Then let $u = x - 1$, $du = dx$:

$$\int \frac{1}{\sqrt{2x - x^2}}\,dx = \int \frac{1}{\sqrt{1 - (x - 1)^2}}\,dx = \int \frac{1}{\sqrt{1 - u^2}}\,du\bigg|^{u=x-1}$$
$$= \arcsin u + C\big|_{u=x-1} = \arcsin (x - 1) + C.$$

c $2x - x^2 = 1 - (x - 1)^2$. Let $u = x - 1$, $du = dx$.

$$\int \frac{dx}{(2x - x^2)^{\frac{3}{2}}} = \int \frac{dx}{[1 - (x - 1)^2]^{\frac{3}{2}}} = \int \frac{du}{(1 - u^2)^{\frac{3}{2}}}\bigg|^{u=x-1}$$
$$= (\text{let}: u = \sin t, du = \cos t\,dt, t = \arcsin u)$$

$$= \int \frac{\cos t\,dt}{\cos^3 t}\bigg|^{t=\arcsin u}$$

$$= \int \sec^2 t\,dt = \tan t + C\bigg|^{t=\arcsin u}$$

$$= \frac{u}{\sqrt{1 - u^2}} + C\bigg|^{u=x-1} = \frac{x - 1}{\sqrt{2x - x^2}} + C$$

Or, after the first few steps, see $\int 41$.

d $4x^2 + 3x + 1 = \left(2x + \frac{3}{4}\right)^2 + \left(\frac{\sqrt{7}}{4}\right)^2$

$$\int = \int \sqrt{\left(2x + \frac{3}{4}\right)^2 + \left(\frac{\sqrt{7}}{4}\right)^2}\,dx$$

$$\left(\text{let } u = 2x + \frac{3}{4},\ du = 2\,dx,\ a = \frac{\sqrt{7}}{4}\right)$$

$$= \frac{1}{2} \int \sqrt{u^2 + a^2}\,du$$

$$= \tfrac{1}{4}[u \sqrt{u^2 + a^2} + a^2 \ln (u + \sqrt{u^2 + a^2})] + C\big|^{u=2x+\frac{3}{4}}$$

$$(\text{by } \int 23)$$

$$= \tfrac{1}{4}[(2x + \tfrac{3}{4}) \sqrt{4x^2 + 3x + 1}$$
$$+ \tfrac{7}{16} \ln (2x + \tfrac{3}{4} + \sqrt{4x^2 + 3x + 1})] + C$$

The remaining frames provide practice in the use of tables of integrals. It is frequently necessary to perform some simplification or initial change of variables before the tabulated formulas can be applied.

156 Use the table of integrals to evaluate $\displaystyle\int \frac{dx}{4x^2 - 1}$.

157 $\int \sqrt{x}\,\sqrt{1 + x^{\frac{3}{2}}}\,dx = ?$ Use the table of integrals after suitable preparation.

158 $\int e^x \sin e^x\,dx = ?$

159 $\displaystyle\int \frac{x\,dx}{1 - x^4} = ?$ Apply the table of integrals after a suitable change of variables.

160 $\int \sin x \cos x \sqrt{2 + 3\sin x}\,dx = ?$

161 $\int x \sin^2 x^2\,dx = ?$

156 First, let $u = 2x$, $du = 2\,dx$; then apply $\int 10$:

$$\int \frac{dx}{4x^2 - 1} = \frac{1}{2} \int \frac{du}{u^2 - 1}\bigg|^{u=2x} = \frac{1}{4} \ln \frac{u-1}{u+1} + C\bigg|^{u=2x}$$
$$= \frac{1}{4} \ln \frac{2x-1}{2x+1} + C.$$

157 Let $u = x^{\frac{3}{2}}$, $du = \frac{3}{2}x^{\frac{1}{2}}\,dx$, then apply $\int 5$:

$$\int \sqrt{x}\,\sqrt{1 + x^{\frac{3}{2}}}\,dx = \frac{2}{3}\int \sqrt{1 + u}\,du\big|^{u=x^{3/2}}$$
$$= \frac{4}{3}(1 + u)^{\frac{3}{2}} + C\big|^{u=x^{3/2}}$$
$$= \frac{4}{3}(1 + x^{\frac{3}{2}})^{\frac{3}{2}} + C.$$

158 Let $u = e^x$, $du = e^x\,dx$.

$$\int e^x \sin e^x\,dx = \int \sin u\,du\big|^{u=e^x}$$
$$= -\cos u + C\big|^{u=e^x} = -\cos e^x + C$$

159 Let $u = x^2$, $du = 2x\,dx$.

$$\int \frac{x\,dx}{1 - x^4} = \frac{1}{2} \int \frac{du}{1 - u^2}\bigg|^{u=x^2}$$
$$= \frac{1}{4} \ln \frac{1+u}{1-u} + C\bigg|^{u=x^2} \qquad \text{(by } \int 9)$$
$$= \frac{1}{4} \ln \frac{1+x^2}{1-x^2} + C$$

160 Let $u = \sin x$, $du = \cos x\,dx$.

$$\int = \int u\,\sqrt{2 + 3u}\,du\bigg|^{u=\sin x}$$
$$= -\frac{2(4 - 9u)(2 + 3u)^{\frac{3}{2}}}{135} + C\big|^{u=\sin x} \qquad \text{(by } \int 20)$$
$$= -\frac{2(4 - 9\sin x)(2 + 3\sin x)^{\frac{3}{2}}}{135} + C$$

161 Let $u = x^2$, $du = 2x\,dx$.

$$\int x \sin^2 x^2\,dx = \frac{1}{2}\int \sin^2 u\,du\big|^{u=x^2}$$
$$= \frac{1}{4}u - \frac{1}{8}\sin 2u + C\big|^{u=x^2} \qquad \text{(by } \int 51)$$
$$= \frac{1}{4}x^2 - \frac{1}{8}\sin 2x^2 + C$$

162 $\int e^{3x} \sin e^x \, dx = ?$

163 $\int \tan^2 x \sec^2 x \ln \tan x \, dx = ?$

164 **a** Evaluate $\displaystyle\int \frac{1}{3x^2 + x + 1} \, dx$ as an instance of $\int 15$.

     b Evaluate $\displaystyle\int \frac{1}{3x^2 + x + 1} \, dx$ by first writing the denominator of the integrand as the sum of two squares.

165 **a** $\displaystyle\int \frac{dx}{e^x + e^{-x}} = ?$

     b $\displaystyle\int \frac{dx}{e^x + e^{-x}} = \int \frac{e^x \, dx}{e^{2x} + 1} = ?$

166 $\displaystyle\int \frac{x \, dx}{\sqrt{x^4 + 2x^2 - 3}} = ?$

162 Let $u = e^x$, $du = e^x\,dx$.

$$\int = \int u^2 \sin u\,du$$
$$= 2u \sin u - (u^2 - 2) \cos u + C\big|_{u=e^x} \qquad \text{(by } \int 74)$$
$$= 2e^x \sin e^x - (e^{2x} - 2) \cos e^x + C$$

163 Let $u = \tan x$, $du = \sec^2 x\,dx$.

$$\int = \int u^2 \ln u\,du$$
$$= \frac{u^3}{3} \ln u - \frac{u^3}{9} + C\big|_{u=\tan x} \qquad \text{(by } \int 89)$$
$$= \frac{\tan^3 x}{3} \ln (\tan x) - \frac{\tan^3 x}{9} + C$$

164 a $\displaystyle\int = \frac{2}{\sqrt{11}} \arctan \frac{6x + 1}{\sqrt{11}} + C$

b $3x^2 + x + 1 = \left(\sqrt{3}\,x + \dfrac{1}{2\sqrt{3}}\right)^2 + \left(\sqrt{\dfrac{11}{12}}\right)^2$

Let $u = \sqrt{3}\,x + \dfrac{1}{2\sqrt{3}}$, $du = \sqrt{3}\,dx$, $c = \sqrt{\dfrac{11}{12}}$.

$$\int = \frac{1}{\sqrt{3}} \int \frac{1}{u^2 + c^2}\,du$$
$$= \frac{1}{\sqrt{3}\,c} \arctan \frac{u}{c} + C_1\big|_{u=\sqrt{3}x+1/2\sqrt{3}} \qquad \text{(by } \int 8)$$
$$= \frac{2}{\sqrt{11}} \arctan \frac{6x + 1}{\sqrt{11}} + C_1$$

165 a This involves some trickery. Proceed to Frame **165b**.

b Let $u = e^x$, $du = e^x\,dx$.

$$\int = \int \frac{du}{u^2 + 1} = \arctan u + C\bigg|^{u=e^x} = \arctan e^x + C$$

166 $x^4 + 2x^2 - 3 = (x^2 + 1)^2 - 4$; let $u = x^2 + 1$, $du = 2x\,dx$.

$$\int = \int \frac{x\,dx}{\sqrt{(x^2 + 1)^2 - 4}} = \frac{1}{2} \int \frac{du}{\sqrt{u^2 - 4}}$$
$$= \ln (u + \sqrt{u^2 - 4}) + C\big|_{u=x^2+1} \qquad \text{(by } \int 24)$$
$$= \ln (x^2 + 1 + \sqrt{x^4 + 2x^2 - 3}) + C$$

167 $\displaystyle\int \frac{x^3 + x}{\sqrt{x^4 + 2x^2 - 3}}\, dx = ?$

168 $\displaystyle\int (x + 2)^3 \sqrt{x^2 + 4x + 5}\, dx = ?$

167 Did you observe in the integrand a function whose derivative appears as a factor?   Let $u = x^4 + 2x^2 - 3$, $du = (4x^3 + 4x)\, dx$.

$\int = \frac{1}{4}\int u^{-\frac{1}{2}}\, du = \frac{1}{2}u^{\frac{1}{2}} + C\big|_{u=x^4+2x^2-3} = \frac{1}{2}\sqrt{x^4 + 2x^2 - 3} + C$

168 $x^2 + 4x + 5 = (x + 2)^2 + 1$.   Let $u = x + 2$, $du = dx$.

$\int = \int (x + 2)^3 \sqrt{(x + 2)^2 + 1}\, dx = \int u^3 \sqrt{u^2 + 1}\, du$
$\quad = (\frac{1}{5}u^2 - \frac{2}{15}) \sqrt{(u^2 + 1)^3} + C\big|_{u=x+2} \qquad \text{(by } \int 34)$
$\quad = [\frac{1}{5}(x + 2)^3 - \frac{2}{15}] \sqrt{(x^2 + 4x + 5)^3} + C$

Without recourse to $\int 34$, the integral $\int u^3 \sqrt{u^2 + 1}\, du$ can be evaluated by first setting $u = \tan t$ to obtain $\int (\sec^2 t - 1) \sec^2 t \sec t \tan t\, dt$, then let $v = \sec t$.

Table of Derivative Formulas

$D_x k = 0$

$D_x x = 1$

$D_x x^a = a x^{a-1}$

$D_x e^x = e^x$

$D_x a^x = a^x \ln a$

$D_x \ln x = \dfrac{1}{x}$

$D_x[f(x) \pm g(x)] = D_x f(x) \pm D_x g(x)$

$D_x[f(x) \cdot g(x)] = f(x) \cdot D_x g(x) + g(x) \cdot D_x f(x)$

$D_x \dfrac{f(x)}{g(x)} = \dfrac{g(x) \cdot D_x f(x) - f(x) \cdot D_x g(x)}{g(x) \cdot g(x)}$

$D_x f[g(x)] = f'[g(x)] \cdot g'(x)$

$D_x[f(u)|^{u=g(x)}] = f'(u)g'(x)|^{u=g(x)}$

　　where $D_u f(u) = f'(u)$ and $D_x g(x) = g'(x)$

$D_x \sin x = \cos x$

$D_x \cos x = -\sin x$

$D_x \tan x = \sec^2 x$

$D_x \cot x = -\csc^2 x$

$D_x \sec x = \sec x \tan x$

$D_x \csc x = -\csc x \cot x$

$D_x \arcsin x = \dfrac{1}{\sqrt{1 - x^2}}$

$D_x \arccos x = \dfrac{-1}{\sqrt{1 - x^2}}$

$D_x \arctan x = \dfrac{1}{1 + x^2}$

Table of Integral Formulas

1　$\int a \cdot f(x)\, dx = a \cdot \int f(x)\, dx$

2　$\int (f(x) + g(x))\, dx = \int f(x)\, dx + \int g(x)\, dx$

3　$\displaystyle\int x^n\, dx = \dfrac{x^{n+1}}{n + 1}$ 　　if $n \neq -1$

4　$\displaystyle\int \dfrac{1}{x}\, dx = \ln x$

5　$\displaystyle\int (a + bx)^n\, dx = \dfrac{(a + bx)^{n+1}}{(n + 1)b}$ 　　if $n \neq -1,\, b \neq 0$

6　$\displaystyle\int \dfrac{dx}{a + bx} = \dfrac{1}{b} \ln (a + bx)$

7　$\displaystyle\int \dfrac{x^2}{a + bx}\, dx = \dfrac{1}{b^3}\left[\tfrac{1}{2}(a + bx)^2 - 2a(a + bx) + a^2 \ln (a + bx)\right]$

8　$\displaystyle\int \dfrac{dx}{c^2 + x^2} = \dfrac{1}{c} \arctan \dfrac{x}{c}$

9　$\displaystyle\int \dfrac{dx}{c^2 - x^2} = \dfrac{1}{2c} \ln \dfrac{c + x}{c - x}$

10　$\displaystyle\int \dfrac{dx}{x^2 - c^2} = \dfrac{1}{2c} \ln \dfrac{x - c}{x + c}$

11 $\displaystyle\int \frac{dx}{(a+bx)(c+dx)} = \frac{1}{ad-bc}\ln\frac{c+dx}{a+bx}$

12 $\displaystyle\int \frac{x\,dx}{(a+bx)(c+dx)} = \frac{1}{ad-bc}\left[\frac{a}{b}\ln(a+bx) - \frac{c}{d}\ln(c+dx)\right]$

13 $\displaystyle\int \frac{dx}{a+bx^2} = \frac{1}{\sqrt{ab}}\arctan\frac{x\sqrt{ab}}{a}$ if $ab > 0$

14 $\displaystyle\int \frac{dx}{a+bx^2} = \frac{1}{2\sqrt{-ab}}\ln\frac{a+x\sqrt{-ab}}{a-x\sqrt{-ab}}$ if $ab < 0$

Let $X = a + bx + cx^2$, $q = 4ac - b^2$

15 $\displaystyle\int \frac{dx}{X} = \frac{2}{\sqrt{q}}\arctan\frac{2cx+b}{\sqrt{q}}$ if $q > 0$

16 $\displaystyle\int \frac{dx}{X^2} = \frac{2cx+b}{qX} + \frac{2c}{q}\int\frac{dx}{X}$

17 $\displaystyle\int \frac{dx}{X^{n+1}} = \frac{2cx+b}{nqX^n} + \frac{2(2n-1)c}{nq}\int\frac{dx}{X^n}$

18 $\displaystyle\int \frac{x\,dx}{X} = \frac{1}{2c}\ln X - \frac{b}{2c}\int\frac{dx}{X}$

19 $\displaystyle\int \frac{x\,dx}{X^{n+1}} = -\frac{2a+bx}{nqX^n} - \frac{b(2n-1)}{nq}\int\frac{dx}{X^n}$

20 $\displaystyle\int x\sqrt{a+bx}\,dx = -\frac{2(2a-3bx)\sqrt{(a+bx)^3}}{15b^2}$

21 $\displaystyle\int x^2\sqrt{a+bx}\,dx = \frac{2(8a^2-12abx+15b^2x^2)\sqrt{(a+bx)^3}}{105b^3}$

22 $\displaystyle\int \frac{x\,dx}{\sqrt{a+bx}} = -\frac{2(2a-bx)}{3b^2}\sqrt{a+bx}$

23 $\displaystyle\int \sqrt{x^2\pm a^2}\,dx = \tfrac{1}{2}[x\sqrt{x^2\pm a^2} \pm a^2\ln(x+\sqrt{x^2\pm a^2})]$

24 $\displaystyle\int \frac{dx}{\sqrt{x^2\pm a^2}} = \ln(x+\sqrt{x^2\pm a^2})$

25 $\displaystyle\int \frac{dx}{x\sqrt{x^2-a^2}} = \frac{1}{a}\arccos\frac{a}{x}$

26 $\displaystyle\int \frac{dx}{x\sqrt{x^2+a^2}} = -\frac{1}{a}\ln\frac{a+\sqrt{x^2+a^2}}{x}$

27 $\displaystyle\int \frac{\sqrt{x^2+a^2}}{x}\,dx = \sqrt{x^2+a^2} - a\ln\frac{a+\sqrt{x^2+a^2}}{x}$

28 $\displaystyle\int \frac{\sqrt{x^2-a^2}}{x}\,dx = \sqrt{x^2-a^2} - a\arccos\frac{a}{x}$

29 $\displaystyle\int \frac{x\,dx}{\sqrt{x^2\pm a^2}} = \sqrt{x^2\pm a^2}$

30 $\int x \sqrt{x^2 \pm a^2}\,dx = \frac{1}{3} \sqrt{(x^2 \pm a^2)^3}$

31 $\displaystyle\int \frac{dx}{\sqrt{(x^2 \pm a^2)^3}} = \frac{\pm x}{a^2 \sqrt{x^2 \pm a^2}}$

32 $\displaystyle\int \frac{x\,dx}{\sqrt{(x^2 \pm a^2)^3}} = \frac{-1}{\sqrt{x^2 \pm a^2}}$

33 $\int x \sqrt{(x^2 \pm a^2)^3}\,dx = \frac{1}{5} \sqrt{(x^2 \pm a^2)^5}$

34 $\int x^3 \sqrt{x^2 + a^2}\,dx = (\frac{1}{5}x^2 - \frac{2}{15}a^2) \sqrt{(x^2 + a^2)^3}$

35 $\displaystyle\int \sqrt{a^2 - x^2}\,dx = \frac{1}{2}\left(x \sqrt{a^2 - x^2} + a^2 \arcsin \frac{x}{a}\right)$

36 $\displaystyle\int \frac{dx}{\sqrt{a^2 - x^2}} = \arcsin \frac{x}{a}$

37 $\displaystyle\int \frac{dx}{x \sqrt{a^2 - x^2}} = -\frac{1}{a} \ln \frac{a + \sqrt{a^2 - x^2}}{x}$

38 $\displaystyle\int \frac{\sqrt{a^2 - x^2}}{x}\,dx = \sqrt{a^2 - x^2} - a \ln \left(a + \frac{\sqrt{a^2 - x^2}}{x}\right)$

39 $\displaystyle\int \frac{x\,dx}{\sqrt{a^2 - x^2}} = -\sqrt{a^2 - x^2}$

40 $\int x \sqrt{a^2 - x^2}\,dx = -\frac{1}{3} \sqrt{(a^2 - x^2)^3}$

41 $\displaystyle\int \frac{dx}{\sqrt{(a^2 - x^2)^3}} = \frac{x}{a^2 \sqrt{a^2 - x^2}}$

42 $\displaystyle\int \frac{x\,dx}{\sqrt{(a^2 - x^2)^3}} = \frac{1}{\sqrt{a^2 - x^2}}$

43 $\int x \sqrt{(a^2 - x^2)^3}\,dx = -\frac{1}{5} \sqrt{(a^2 - x^2)^5}$

44 $\displaystyle\int \frac{dx}{(a + bx + cx^2)^{3/2}} = \frac{2(2cx + b)}{(4ac - b^2) \sqrt{a + bx + cx^2}}$

45 $\int \sin x\,dx = -\cos x$

46 $\int \cos x\,dx = \sin x$

47 $\int \tan x\,dx = -\ln \cos x$

48 $\int \cot x\,dx = \ln \sin x$

49 $\int \sec x\,dx = \ln (\sec x + \tan x)$

50 $\int \csc x\,dx = \ln (\csc x - \cot x)$

51 $\int \sin^2 x\,dx = \frac{1}{2}x - \frac{1}{2} \sin x \cos x = \frac{1}{2}x - \frac{1}{4} \sin 2x$

52 $\int \sin^3 x\,dx = -\frac{1}{3} (\cos x)(\sin^2 x + 2)$

53 $\displaystyle\int \sin^n x\,dx = \frac{1}{n}\left[-\sin^{n-1} x \cos x + (n - 1) \int \sin^{n-2} x\,dx \right]$

54 $\int \cos^2 x\,dx = \frac{1}{2}x + \frac{1}{2} \sin x \cos x = \frac{1}{2}x + \frac{1}{4} \sin 2x$

55 $\int \cos^3 x\,dx = \frac{1}{3} (\sin x)(\cos^2 x + 2)$

56 $\displaystyle\int \cos^n x\,dx = \frac{1}{n}\left[\cos^{n-1} x \sin x + (n - 1) \int \cos^{n-2} x\,dx \right]$

57 $\displaystyle\int \sin (a + bx)\,dx = -\frac{1}{b} \cos (a + bx)$

58 $\displaystyle\int \cos (a + bx)\,dx = \frac{1}{b} \sin (a + bx)$

59 $\displaystyle\int \frac{dx}{\cos^n x}\, dx = \frac{1}{n-1}\frac{\sin x}{\cos^{n-1} x} + \frac{n-2}{n-1}\int \frac{dx}{\cos^{n-2} x}$ or

$\displaystyle\int \sec^n x\, dx = \frac{1}{n-1}\sec^{n-2} x \tan x + \frac{n-2}{n-1}\int \sec^{n-2} x\, dx$

60 $\displaystyle\int \sin mx \sin nx\, dx = \frac{\sin (m-n)x}{2(m-n)} - \frac{\sin (m+n)x}{2(m+n)}$ if $m^2 \neq n^2$

61 $\displaystyle\int \cos mx \cos nx\, dx = \frac{\sin (m-n)x}{2(m-n)} + \frac{\sin (m+n)x}{2(m+n)}$ if $m^2 \neq n^2$

62 $\int \sin x \cos x\, dx = \frac{1}{2}\sin^2 x$

63 $\displaystyle\int \sin mx \cos nx\, dx = -\frac{\cos (m-n)x}{2(m-n)} - \frac{\cos (m+n)x}{2(m+n)}$ if $m^2 \neq n^2$

64 $\displaystyle\int \sin x \cos^m x\, dx = -\frac{\cos^{m+1} x}{m+1}$

65 $\displaystyle\int \sin^m x \cos x\, dx = \frac{\sin^{m+1} x}{m+1}$

66 $\displaystyle\int \frac{\sin x}{\cos^2 x}\, dx = \int \sec x \tan x\, dx = \sec x$

67 $\int \tan^2 x\, dx = \tan x - x$

68 $\displaystyle\int \tan^n x\, dx = \frac{\tan^{n-1} x}{n-1} - \int \tan^{n-2} x\, dx$ if $n \neq 1$

69 $\int \cot^2 x\, dx = -\cot x - x$

70 $\displaystyle\int \cot^n x\, dx = -\frac{\cot^{n-1} x}{n-1} - \int \cot^{n-2} x\, dx$ if $n \neq 1$

71 $\int \sec^2 x\, dx = \tan x$

72 $\int \csc^2 x\, dx = -\cot x$

73 $\int x \sin x\, dx = \sin x - x \cos x$

74 $\int x^2 \sin x\, dx = 2x \sin x - (x^2 - 2) \cos x$

75 $\int x^3 \sin x\, dx = (3x^2 - 6) \sin x - (x^3 - 6x) \cos x$

76 $\int x^m \sin x\, dx = -x^m \cos x + m \int x^{m-1} \cos x\, dx$

77 $\int x \cos x\, dx = \cos x + x \sin x$

78 $\int x^2 \cos x\, dx = 2x \cos x + (x^2 - 2) \sin x$

79 $\int x^3 \cos x\, dx = (3x^2 - 6) \cos x + (x^3 - 6x) \sin x$

80 $\int x^m \cos x\, dx = x^m \sin x - m \int x^{m-1} \sin x\, dx$

81 $\int \arcsin x\, dx = x \arcsin x + \sqrt{1 - x^2}$

82 $\int \arccos x\, dx = x \arccos x - \sqrt{1 - x^2}$

83 $\int \arctan x\, dx = x \arctan x - \frac{1}{2}\ln (1 + x^2)$

84 $\displaystyle\int \arcsin \frac{x}{a}\, dx = x \arcsin \frac{x}{a} + \sqrt{a^2 - x^2}$

85 $\displaystyle\int \arccos \frac{x}{a}\, dx = x \arccos \frac{x}{a} - \sqrt{a^2 - x^2}$

86 $\displaystyle\int \arctan \frac{x}{a}\, dx = x \arctan \frac{x}{a} - \frac{a}{2}\ln (a^2 + x^2)$

87 $\int \ln x \, dx = x \ln x - x$

88 $\int x \ln x \, dx = \dfrac{x^2}{2} \ln x - \dfrac{x^2}{4}$

89 $\int x^2 \ln x \, dx = \dfrac{x^3}{3} \ln x - \dfrac{x^3}{9}$

90 $\int x^p \ln (ax) \, dx = \dfrac{x^{p+1}}{p+1} \ln (ax) - \dfrac{x^{p+1}}{(p+1)^2}$ if $p \neq -1$

91 $\int \dfrac{(\ln x)^n}{x} \, dx = \dfrac{1}{n+1} (\ln x)^{n+1}$

92 $\int \dfrac{dx}{x \ln x} = \ln (\ln x)$

93 $\int e^x \, dx = e^x$

94 $\int e^{-x} \, dx = -e^{-x}$

95 $\int e^{ax} \, dx = \dfrac{1}{a} e^{ax}$

96 $\int x e^{ax} \, dx = \dfrac{e^{ax}}{a^2} (ax - 1)$

97 $\int x^m e^{ax} \, dx = \dfrac{x^m e^{ax}}{a} - \dfrac{m}{a} \int x^{m-1} e^{ax} \, dx$

98 $\int e^{ax} \sin px \, dx = \dfrac{e^{ax}(a \sin px - p \cos px)}{a^2 + p^2}$

99 $\int e^{ax} \cos px \, dx = \dfrac{e^{ax}(a \cos px + p \sin px)}{a^2 + p^2}$